the brain
puzzle flip pad

over 120 puzzles with the answers on the flip side

PaRragon

Bath · New York · Cologne · Melbourne · Delhi
Hong Kong · Shenzhen · Singapore · Amsterdam

D0284713

This edition published by Parragon Books Ltd in 2014

Parragon Books Ltd
Chartist House
15–17 Trim Street
Bath BA1 1HA, UK
www.parragon.com

ISBN 978-1-4454-5933-2

Printed in China

Wordfit

Can you fit all of the listed words into the grid below? One letter is already in place, to get you off to a good start.

3 Letters
ANY
INN
ITS
SIP

4 Letters
ARMY
AXLE
IDEA
POLL
REST
SNUB

5 Letters
BELLS
CHINA
DEALT
FAINT
INNER
SOLAR

6 Letters
CIRCUS
PATINA
STOREY
THESIS

7 Letters
AERATED
BANANAS
COOKERY
INTEGER
PARAPET
VOLCANO

8 Letters
ETHEREAL
ORATORIO

9 Letters
MENAGERIE
UNBALANCE

10 Letters
EXTRANEOUS
RHEUMATISM

INN
ITS
SIP

4 Letters
ARMY
AXLE
IDEA
POLL
REST
SNUB

5 Letters
BELLS
CHINA
DEALT
FAINT
INNER
SOLAR

6 Letters
CIRCUS
PATINA
STOREY
THESIS

7 Letters
BANANAS
COOKERY
INTEGER
PARAPET

Well Spotted

Some of the circles in this puzzle are already black. Fill in more white circles, so that the number of black circles totals the number inside the area they surround.

Every black circle surrounding an area with a number higher than '1' needs to be next to another black circle surrounding the same area. When solving, it may help to put a small dot into any circle you know should not be filled.

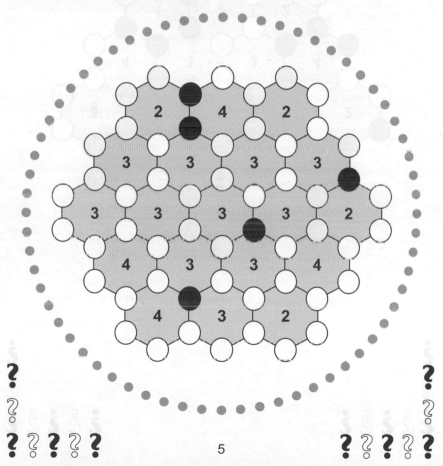

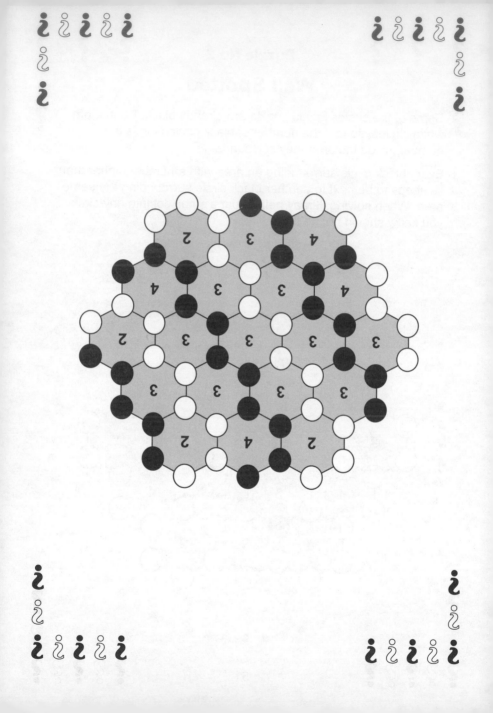

Alphafill

Place 25 different letters of the alphabet, one per circle, in order to spell out the listed words. Words are formed by moving between adjacent circles along the connecting lines, either horizontally, vertically or diagonally in any direction.

Begin by crossing out the letters already in place, together with the one letter that doesn't appear in any of the words.

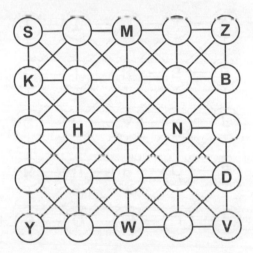

A B C D E F G H I J K L M
N O P Q R S T U V W X Y Z

BONE	JOB	PANE	TREND
CHAIR	LIAR	PARITY	VEXED
FOND	MUSK	SQUANDER	WIRED
HARE	OZONE	SUCH	WRIT

Puzzle No 3

Alphafill

Place 26 different letters of the alphabet, one per circle, in order to spell out the listed words. Words are formed by moving between adjacent circles along the connecting lines, either horizontally, vertically or diagonally in any direction.

Begin by crossing out the letters already in place, together with the one letter that doesn't appear in any of the words

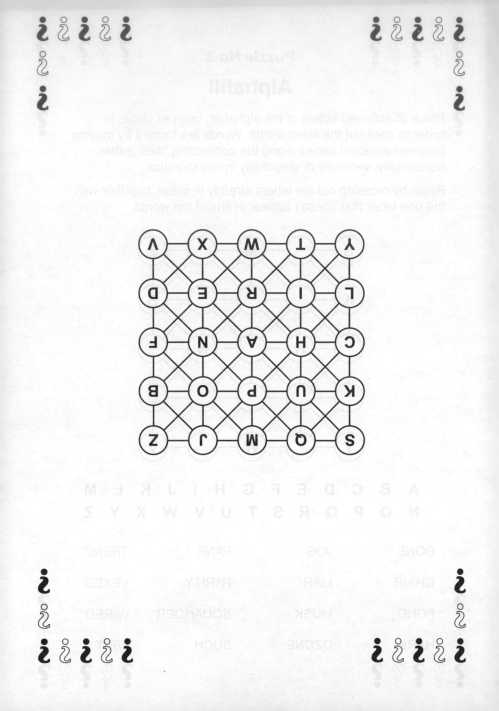

A B C D E F G H I J K L M
N O P Q R S T U V W X Y Z

BONE	JOB	PANE	TREND
CHAIR	LIAR	PARITY	VEXED
FOND	MUSK	SQUANDER	WIRED
	OZONE	SUCH	

7.

Hoshi

The numbers 1 to 9 must be placed into the individual cells of each of the six large triangles.

No digit can appear more than once in any horizontal row or diagonal line of any length, even those rows and lines that are interrupted by the central hexagon.

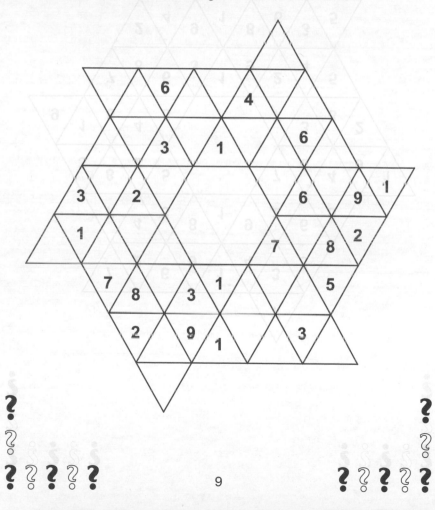

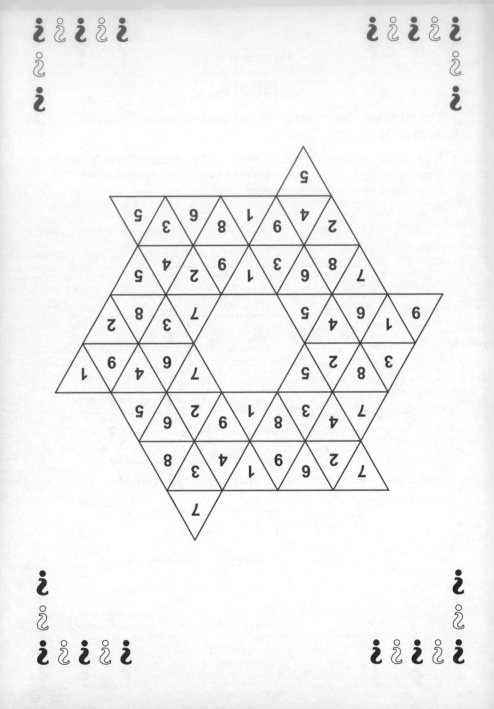

Pieceword

This crossword has been cut into 24 pieces. Can you reassemble it by placing the remaining 20 pieces?

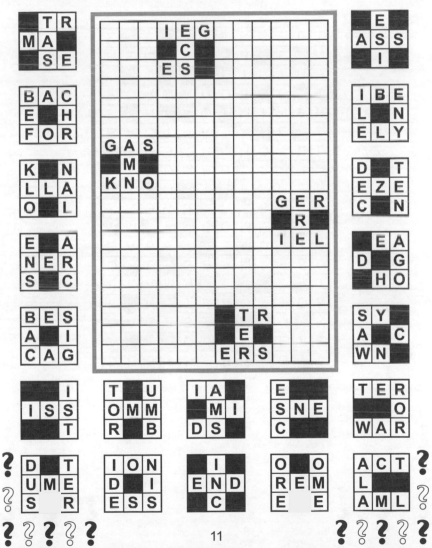

Pieceword

This crossword has been cut into 24 pieces. Can you reassemble it by placing the remaining 20 pieces?

S Bend

Place the letters of each word, one per cell, so that every word flows In a clockwise direction around a number. Where the hexagons of one word overlap with those of another, the letter in each cell is common to both.

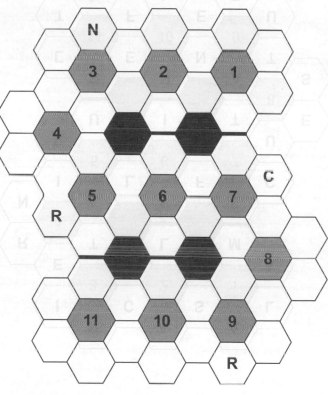

BURIAL		RETAIN
FENNEL	NATURE	SALAMI
FOIBLE	OFFCUT	SILICA
INCITE	REFUTE	STATUE

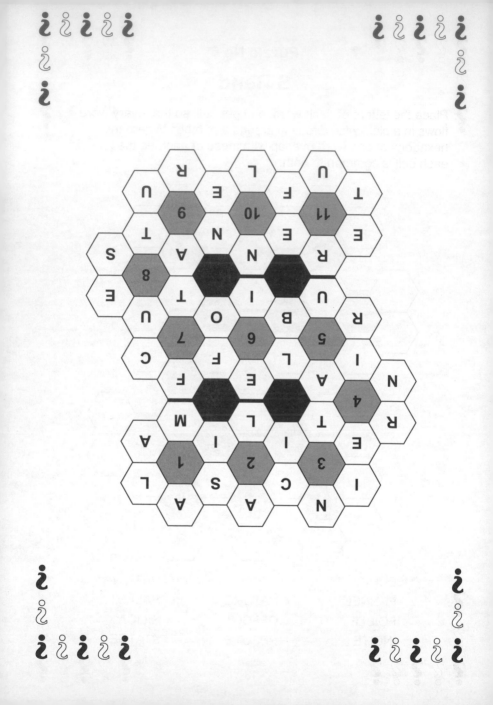

Loose Vowels

Every clue in this crossword consists of its solution, with the letters in order but minus its vowels. Your task is to replace the vowels; gd lck!

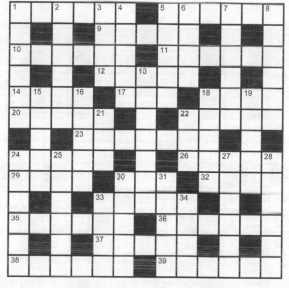

ACROSS

1 STT (6)
5 PDL (6)
9 NTR (5)
10 SMN (6)
11 CSN (6)
12 RRL (5)
14 TM (4)
17 N (3)
18 HR (4)
20 LRD (5)
22 LND (5)
23 NTHR (7)
24 SRN (5)
26 GNS (5)
29 CD (4)
30 NT (3)
32 DR (4)
33 SMR (5)
35 CPL (6)
36 PNN (6)
37 NST (5)
38 RLD (6)
39 RCD (6)

DOWN

1 BSL (6)
2 TMBR (6)
3 TR (4)
4 NN (5)
5 PCN (5)
6 RL (4)
7 DRVN (6)
8 VKD (6)
13 RTN (7)
15 TNC (5)
16 MND (5)
18 HRD (5)
19 RCR (5)
21 DN (3)
22 LG (3)
24 SCR (6)
25 RBK (6)
27 NTV (6)
28 SNC (6)
30 MND (5)
31 TPR (5)
33 SL (4)
34 RT (4)

4 NN (5)
5 FCN (6)
6 FL (4)
7 DRVN (6)
8 VKD (6)
13 RTN (7)
15 TNG (6)
16 MNG (4)

Skyscrapers

Place the numbers 1 to 7 into each row and column. Each number represents a skyscraper of that many floors. Organize the skyscrapers in such a way that the given number outside the grid represents the number of buildings which can be seen from that point, looking only at that number's row or column.

A skyscraper with a lower number of floors cannot hide a higher building, but one with a higher number of floors always hides any building behind it.

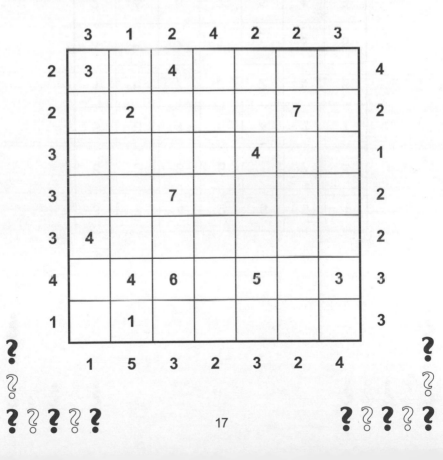

3	7	4	2	6	5	1
6	2	3	5	1	7	4
5	3	1	6	4	2	7
1	6	7	3	2	4	5
4	5	2	1	7	3	6
2	4	6	7	5	1	3
7	1	5	4	3	6	2

Number Cruncher

Just like a regular crossword, but with numbers as answers!

ACROSS

1. One eighteenth of 26 Across (3)
4. 14 Down minus 15 (3)
6. 19 Down plus 3025 (5)
9. 12 Across plus 15 Across plus 21 Across (2)
11. 1 Across minus 27 Down (3)
12. Five ninths of 15 Across (2)
13. One eighteenth of 28 Across (2)
15. 24 Across multiplied by two (2)
16. 5 Down multiplied by nine (4)
17. 28 Across multiplied by five (4)
18. 2 Down minus 7 Down (2)
20. 27 Down minus 7 Down (2)
21. One third of 12 Across (2)
22. One third of 28 Across (3)
24. One twelfth of 28 Across (2)
26. 22 Across multiplied by 21 Down (5)
28. Inches in nine yards (3)
29. 9 Across plus 11 Across plus two (3)

DOWN

1. 5 Down plus 27 Down (3)
2. One quarter of 28 Across (2)
3. 20 cubed (4)
4. 2 Down plus two (2)
5. 9 cubed plus 11 squared (3)
7. One third of 23 Down (2)
8. 12 Across plus 27 Down (2)
10. 5 Down multiplied by 27 Down (5)
12. 185 squared minus square root of 169 (5)
14. 12 Across plus 22 Across plus 25 Down (3)
15. 24 squared minus 26 Down (3)
19. 9 Across squared plus 212 (4)
21. 12 Across plus 22 Across plus five (3)
22. 30 per cent of 50 (2)
23. 8 Down plus one third of 22 Down (2)
25. 21 Down multiplied by five (3)
26. Pounds in one stone (2)
27. Seven squared (2)

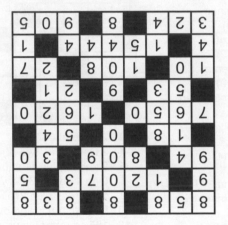

Round Numbers

Fill the circles so that every row and column of eight circles contains the numbers 1–8 inclusive. The shaded circles contain odd numbers 1, 3, 5 and 7, and the white circles contain even numbers 2, 4, 6 and 8. Some of the numbers are already in place.

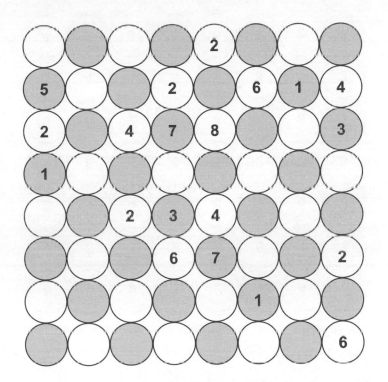

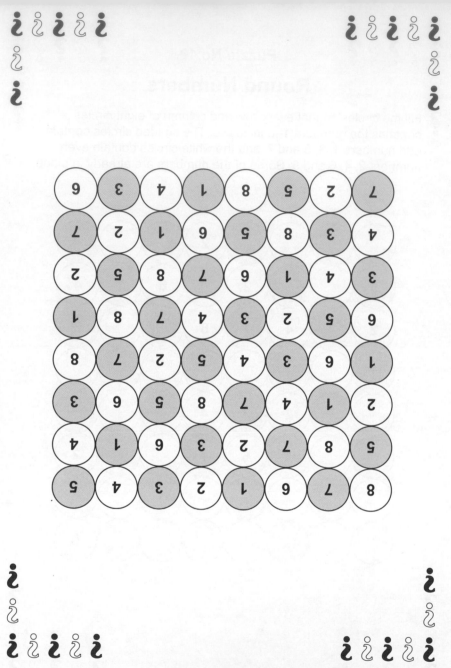

Puzzle No 11

Combiku

Each horizontal row and vertical column should contain five different shapes and five different numbers. Every square will contain one number and one shape and no combination may be repeated anywhere else in the puzzle: for example, if a square has both a 4 and a star, then no other square will contain both a 4 and a star.

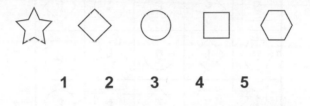

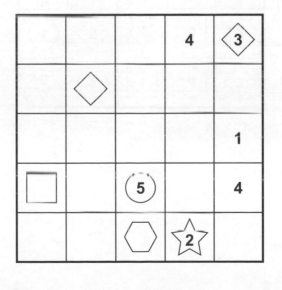

23

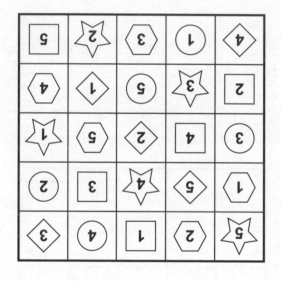

Puzzle No 12

Latin Square

Fill the grid with numbers from 1 to 6, so that each number appears exactly once in every row and every column.

The clues refer to the sum of the numbers in the squares mentioned: for example, B C D 1 = 14 means that the numbers in squares B1, C1 and D1 add up to 14.

1 C 1 2 = 3	**5** A 3 4 = 8	**9** D E 3 = 6
2 B C D 6 = 8	**6** E 4 5 = 9	**10** C D 5 = 8
3 F 4 5 6 = 8	**7** A 5 6 = 3	**11** D 1 2 = 11
4 E F 1 = 7	**8** B 1 2 = 7	**12** E F 2 = 4

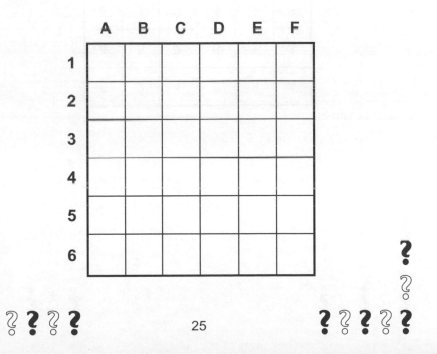

6	2	1	5	3	4
4	5	2	6	1	3
5	1	3	4	2	6
3	4	6	2	5	1
1	6	5	3	4	2
2	3	4	1	6	5

Battleships

Can you place the vessels into the diagram? Some parts of vessels or sea squares have already been filled in. A number to the left or above a row or column refers to the number of occupied squares in that row or column.

Any vessel may be positioned horizontally or vertically, but no part of a vessel touches part of any other vessel, either horizontally, vertically or diagonally.

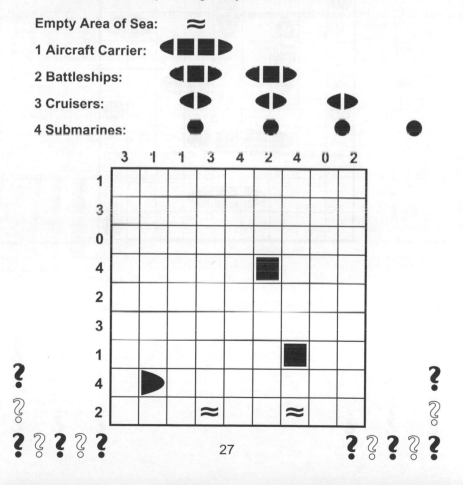

Empty Area of Sea:

1 Aircraft Carrier:

2 Battleships:

3 Cruisers:

4 Submarines:

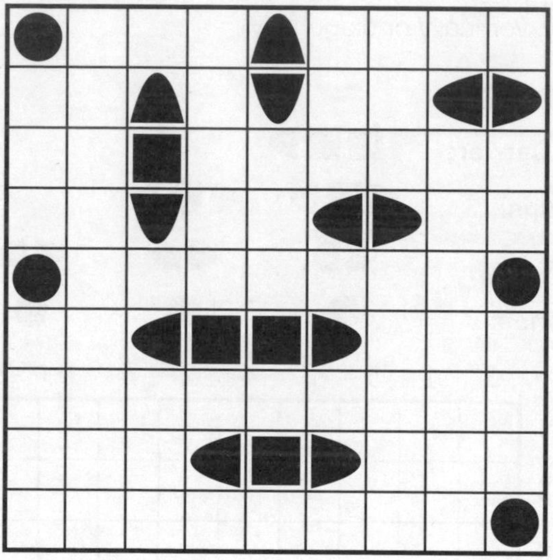

Arrowword

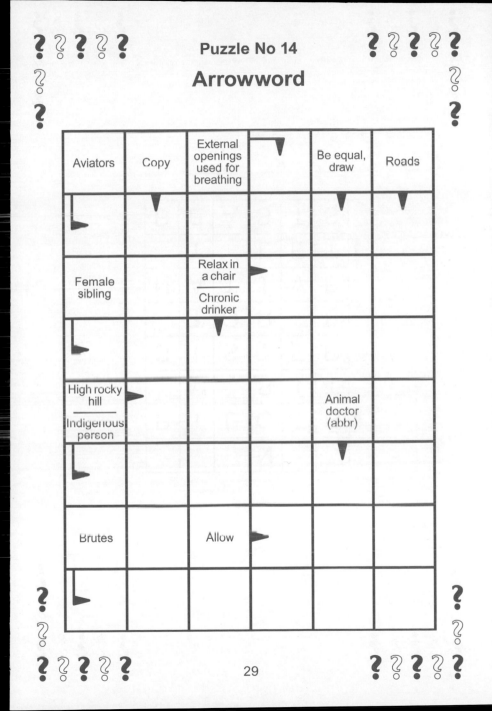

Aviators	Copy	External openings used for breathing		Be equal, draw	Roads
Female sibling		Relax in a chair / Chronic drinker			
High rocky hill / Indigenous person				Animal doctor (abbr)	
Brutes		Allow			

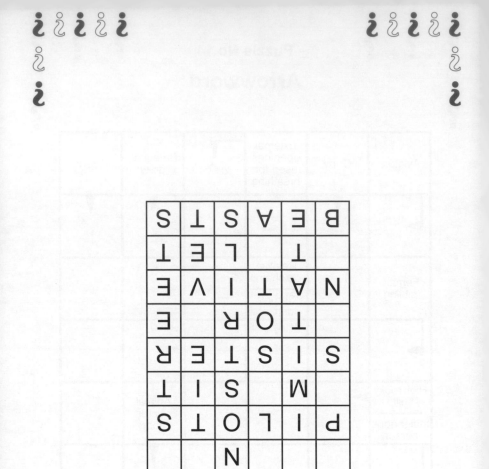

Shape Up

Every row and column in this grid originally contained one circle, one diamond, one square, one triangle and two blank squares, although not necessarily in that order.

Every symbol with a black arrow refers to the first of the four symbols encountered when travelling in the direction of the arrow. Every symbol with a white arrow refers to the second of the four symbols encountered in the direction of the arrow.

Can you complete the original grid?

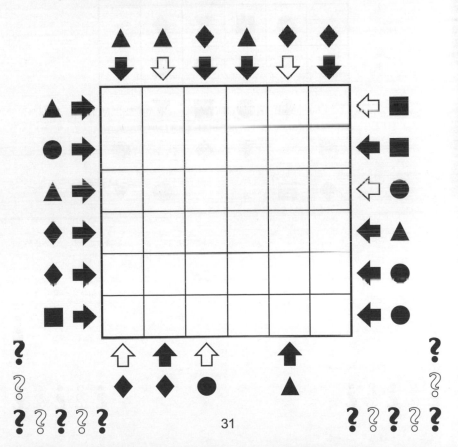

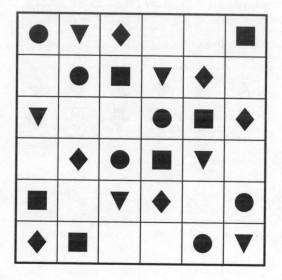

Domino Placement

A standard set of 28 dominoes has been laid out as shown. Can you draw in the edges of them all? The check-box is provided as an aid and the domino already placed may help.

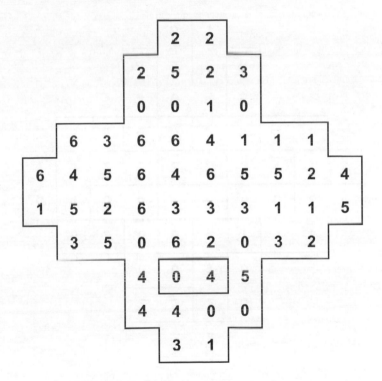

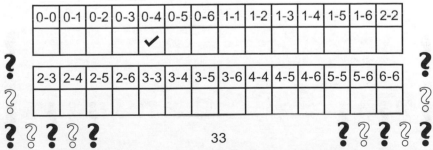

0-0	0-1	0-2	0-3	0-4	0-5	0-6	1-1	1-2	1-3	1-4	1-5	1-6	2-2
				✓									

2-3	2-4	2-5	2-6	3-3	3-4	3-5	3-6	4-4	4-5	4-6	5-5	5-6	6-6

		2	2				
	2	5	2	3			
	0	0	1	0			
	6	3	6	6	4	1	1	1
6	4	5	6	4	6	5	5	2	4
1	5	2	6	3	3	3	1	1	5
	3	5	0	6	2	0	3	2
		4	0	4	5		
		4	4	0	0		
			3	1			

Codeword

Every letter in this crossword has been replaced by a number, the number remaining the same for that letter wherever it occurs in the grid. Can you substitute numbers for letters and complete the crossword? It may help to cross off the letters either side of the grid to keep track of progress, and the reference box showing which numbers have been decoded can also aid solving. Three letters have already been entered into the grid, to help you on your way.

A	10	23	11	12	14	15	17		5	8	14	0	2	**N**
B	7		19		19		11		11		15		15	**O**
C	15	10	9	19	11		19	9	17	8	24	9	3	**P**
D	14		12		10		14		9		8		21	**Q**
E	14	19	11	21	9	3	18		7	16	5	1	18	**R**
F	9			26	9	19	15		19		9			**S**
G	3	9	11	6	9	12		17	11	12	11	21	9	**T**
H		1		16		25	10	8	12				25	**U**
I	17	9	11	12	25		11	14	14	19	11 A	5 C	14 T	**V**
J	11		22		15		10		8		4		16	**W**
K	20	16	22	8	7	9	9		2	16	15	14	11	**X**
L	15		9		13		19		16		1		19	**Y**
M	19	23	18	17	9		25	5	9	12	9	19	18	**Z**

1	2	3	4	5 C	6	7	8	9	10	11 A	12	13
14 T	15	16	17	18	19	20	21	22	23	24	25	26

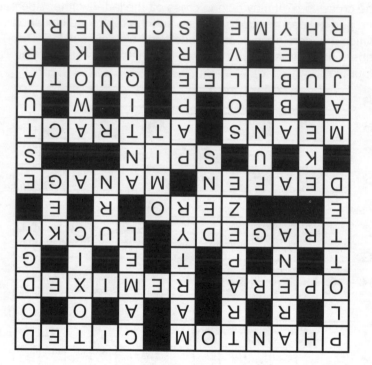

Calcudoku

Each row and column should contain the numbers 1–6. The numbers placed in a heavily outlined set of squares may be repeated, but must produce the calculation in the top left corner, using the mathematical symbol provided. So, for example, when multiplied, the numbers 3 and 4 total 12:

x12	
4	3

Any block of one square will contain the number in the top left corner.

x40	/3		x12	−2	
		/4		+9	x15
+8	+11		x15		
					+9
+8		+11		/5	
	x24				

5	1	3	2	6	4
4	2	1	6	3	5
6	5	4	1	2	3
2	6	5	3	4	1
3	4	6	5	1	2
1	3	2	4	5	6

Piecework

Place all of the pieces into the grid. Any may be rotated or flipped over, but none may touch another, not even diagonally at a corner.

The numbers outside the grid refer to the number of consecutive black squares; and each block is separated from the others by at least one white square. For instance, '3 2' could refer to a row with either none or any number of white squares, then three black squares, then at least one white square, then two more black squares, followed by either none or any number of white squares.

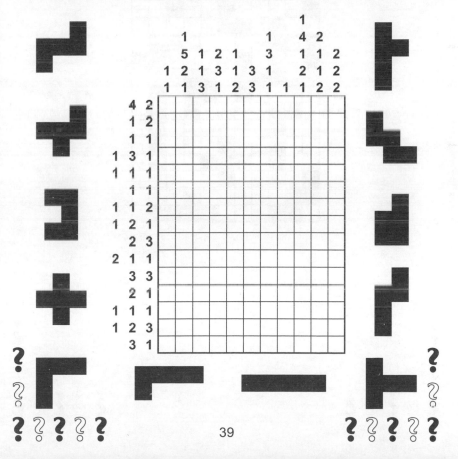

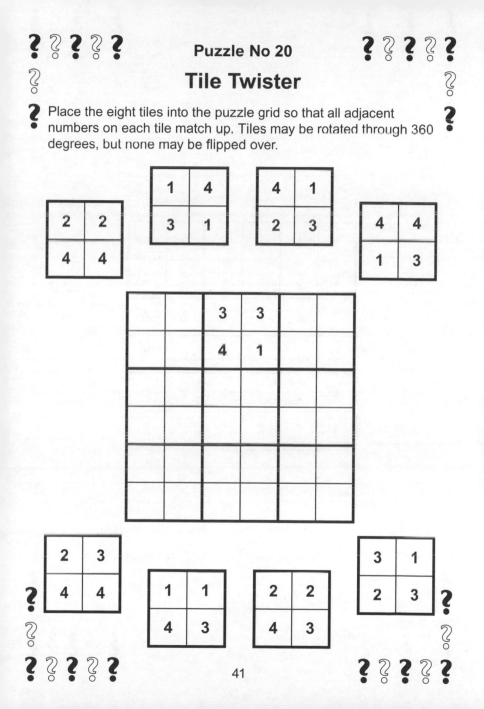

Tile Twister

Place the eight tiles into the puzzle grid so that all adjacent numbers on each tile match up. Tiles may be rotated through 360 degrees, but none may be flipped over.

2	3	3	3	3	1
4	4	4	1	1	4
4	4	4	1	1	4
2	2	2	3	3	4
2	2	2	3	3	4
4	3	3	1	1	1

Box Clever

When the shape below is folded to form a cube, just one of the lettered alternatives can be produced. Which?

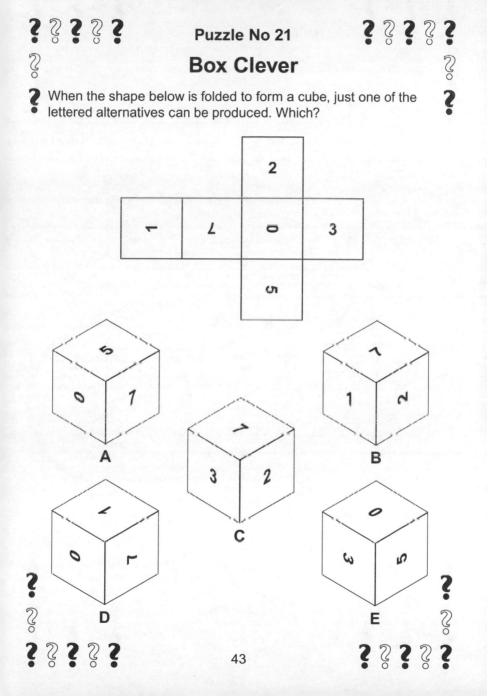

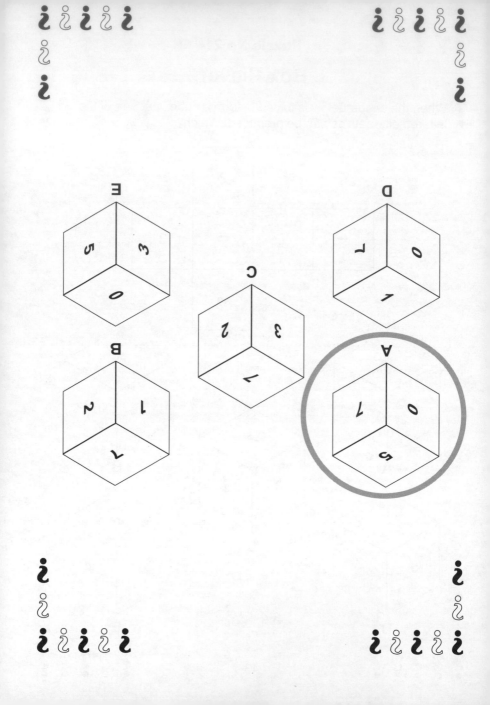

Four Out of Three

Fill the grid using the three-letter words. When they've been entered correctly, three four-letter words will be revealed in each row, reading from left to right.

E	V	E				T	E	N			
P	A	N				I	R	K			
S	A	G				A	N	Y			
G	O	O				G	E	L			
W	A	S				R	E	F			
M	A	N				D	O	G			
P	U	N				E	R	A			
S	U	E				S	E	W			
T	I	N				M	O	P			
P	E	R				E	A	R			

HIP	YAM	RAY	OUR	AID
OVA	KID	OAF	YEW	ERE
VOW	EWE	TEA	RAN	HOG
ROD	FUR	AWE	LAD	NEW

E	V	E	R	A	N	T	E	N	O	V	A
P	A	N	E	W	E	I	R	K	N	E	W
S	A	G	A	W	E	A	N	Y	O	U	R
G	O	O	F	U	R	G	E	L	O	A	F
W	A	S	H	O	G	R	E	F	R	A	Y
M	A	N	E	R	E	D	O	G	L	A	D
P	U	N	Y	E	W	E	R	A	V	O	W
S	U	E	T	E	A	S	E	W	H	I	P
T	I	N	Y	A	M	M	O	P	R	O	D
P	E	R	K	I	D	E	A	R	A	I	D

Light Up

Place circles (representing light bulbs) in some of the empty squares, in such a way that no two bulbs shine on each other, until every square of the grid is lit up. A bulb sends rays of light horizontally and vertically, illuminating its entire row and column unless its light is blocked by a black cell.

Some black cells contain numbers, indicating how many light bulbs are in adjacent squares either immediately above, below, to the right or to the left. Bulbs placed diagonally adjacent to a numbered cell do not contribute to the bulb count. An unnumbered black cell may have any number of light bulbs adjacent to it, or none at all, and not all light bulbs are necessarily clued via black squares.

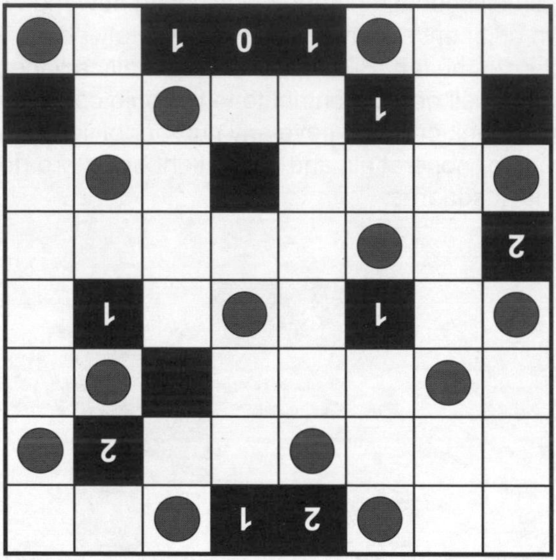

Kakuro

Using single digits from 1 to 9 inclusive, fill the grid so that the numbers in each block add up to the total in the box above or to the left of it. No digit may be used twice in a block. The same digit may occur more than once in a row or column, but it must be in a separate block.

Slitherlink

Draw a single continuous loop, by connecting the dots. No line may cross the path of another.

The figure inside each set of any four surrounding dots indicates the total number of surrounding lines.

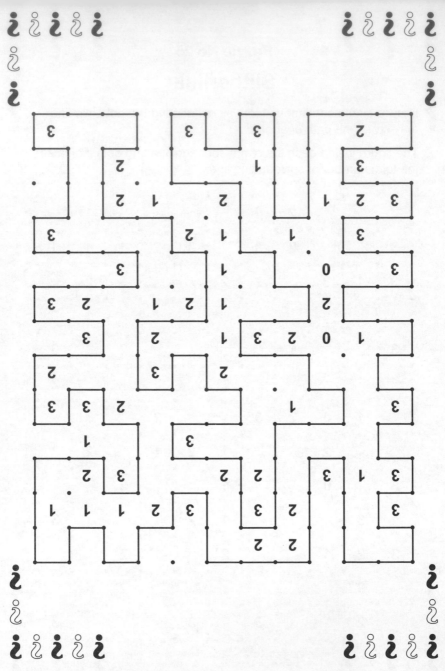

Egg Timer

Can you complete this puzzle in the time that it takes to boil an egg? The answers to the clues are anagrams of the words immediately above and below, plus or minus a letter.

1 Mystified

2 Legendary

3 Cutting edge of a knife

4 Distribute

5 Forest clearing

6 Suspend freely

7 Looked at quickly

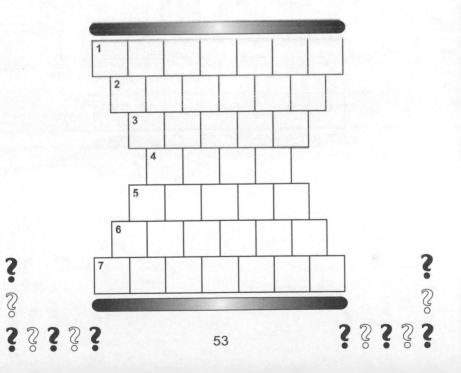

General Knowledge Crossword

ACROSS

4 Glowing fragment of wood or coal left from a fire (5)

7 Breathe out (6)

8 French word for Christmas (4)

9 Cereal grain used in distilling (4)

11 Biblical garden (4)

14 Occupant of 11 Across (4)

15 Person from a foreign country (5)

16 Desert which straddles Mongolia and China (4)

17 Verdi opera with an Egyptian theme (4)

20 Submerged ridge of rock or coral (4)

22 Character in Shakespeare's *Othello* (4)

23 Country formerly known as British Honduras (6)

24 Prince who abducted Helen of Troy (5)

DOWN

1 Divisions of a pound sterling (5)

2 Country, capital Santiago (5)

3 Edible smooth-skinned fruit with a single hard stone (4)

5 US state bordering Canada (7)

6 Green transparent form of beryl (7)

10 Girl in Lewis Carroll's famous stories (5)

12 Series of pictures representing a continuous scene (7)

13 Capital of Kenya (7)

18 Country in which Mumbai is situated (5)

19 Church associated with a convent (5)

21 Bloodsucking parasite (4)

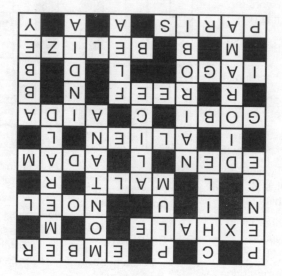

Around the Block

You won't need a starting block to get you under way, because it isn't a race! Just arrange the six-letter solutions to the clues into the six blocks around each clue number.

Write the answers in a clockwise or anticlockwise direction and you'll find that the last answer fits into the first; the problem is to decide in which square to put the first letter of each word...

1 Slender, constricted

2 Blossom, bloom

3 Favour, like better

4 Influence, make a difference

5 Male parent

6 Towards the tail end of a ship

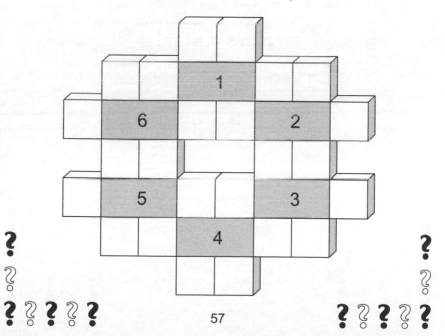

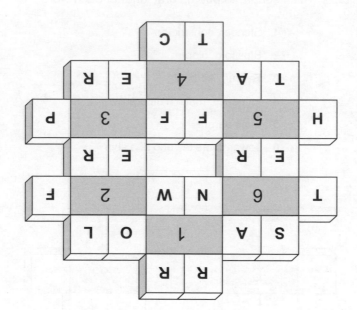

1 Narrow (c), 2 Flower (a/c), 3 Prefer (c or a/c), 4 Affect (c), 5 Father (c), 6 Astern (a/c)

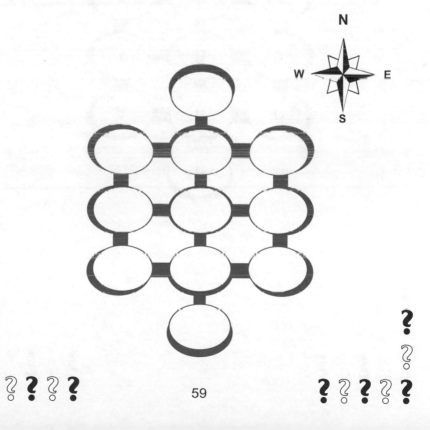

Eliminator

Every oval shape contains a different letter of the alphabet from A to K inclusive. Use the clues to determine their locations. Reference in the clues to 'due' means in any location along the same horizontal or vertical line.

1 A is due north of I, which is due west of B.

2 C is due west of G, which is due south of J.

3 E is due north of H, which is due west of D, which is due east of A.

4 F is due west of C, which is due north of K.

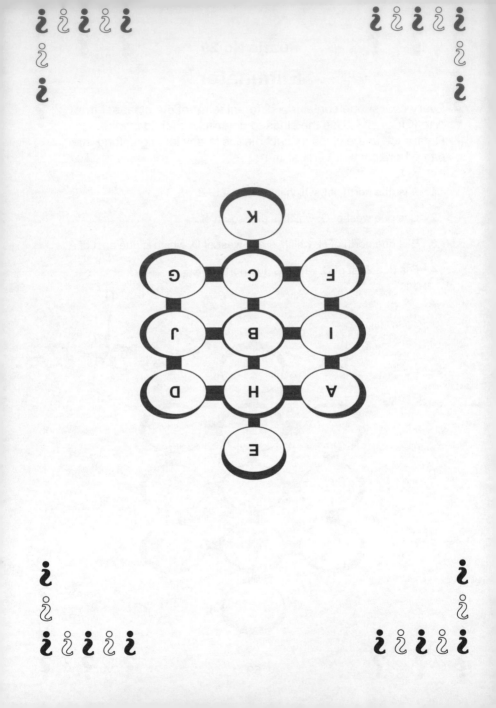

Figure It Out

Every square in the grid is to be filled with a single digit number from 1 to 9 – each of those numbers being used four times. Use the clues to complete the grid, bearing in mind that the same number must not appear in two adjacent (touching) squares either across or down. If the same number is used more than once in any row across or column down, it is stated in the relevant clue.

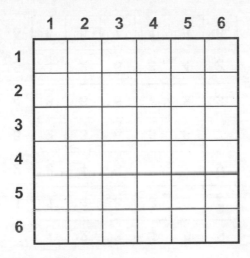

ACROSS

1 Two *eights*. No *six* or *seven*.

2 Two *ones*. Two *nines*.

3 Consecutive numbers placed in order.

4 Two *fives*. Two *threes* are the lowest numbers.

5 Two *twos*. Two *fours*. No odd numbers.

6 *Six* is the only even number.

DOWN

1 Total twenty-seven.

2 Total twenty-one.

3 Total thirty-nine.

4 Two *ones*. *Eight* is the only even number.

5 Consecutive numbers placed in order.

6 Two *twos*.

	1	2	3	4	5	6
1	1	4	8	9	8	2
2	8	1	9	1	7	9
3	2	3	4	5	6	7
4	3	6	5	7	5	3
5	4	2	6	8	4	2
6	9	5	7	1	3	6

Round Up

The number in each circle is the sum of the two numbers below it. Just work out the missing numbers in every circle!

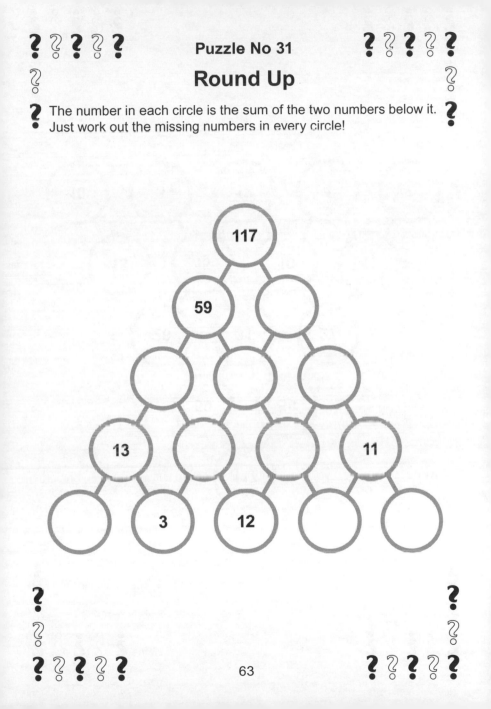

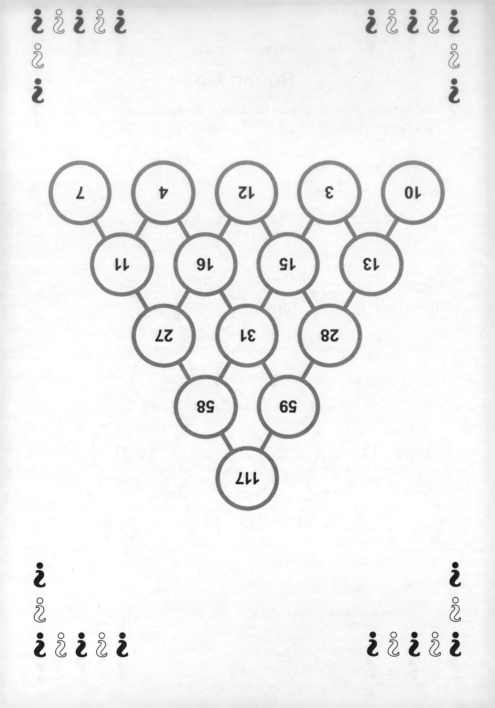

Windows

There is a four-letter word hidden in each of the boxes on the left that can only be revealed by matching each box with its correct window-strip on the right. Can you match all ten?

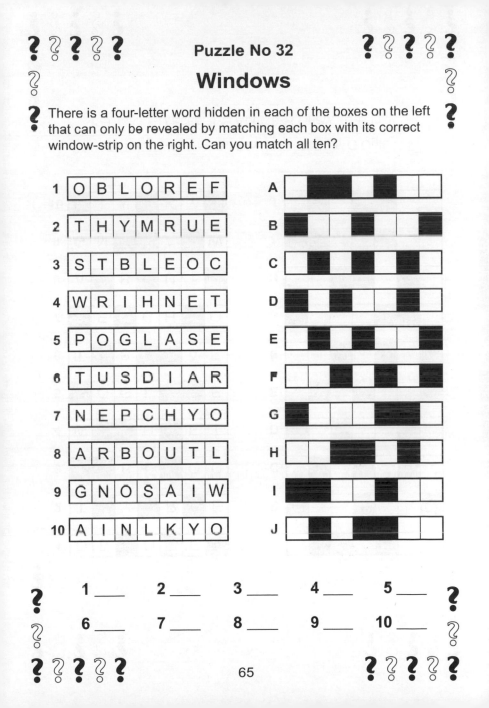

1 O B L O R E F   A

2 T H Y M R U E   B

3 S T B L E O C   C

4 W R I H N E T   D

5 P O G L A S E   E

6 T U S D I A R   F

7 N E P C H Y O   G

8 A R B O U T L   H

9 G N O S A I W   I

10 A I N L K Y O   J

1 ___   2 ___   3 ___   4 ___   5 ___

6 ___   7 ___   8 ___   9 ___   10 ___

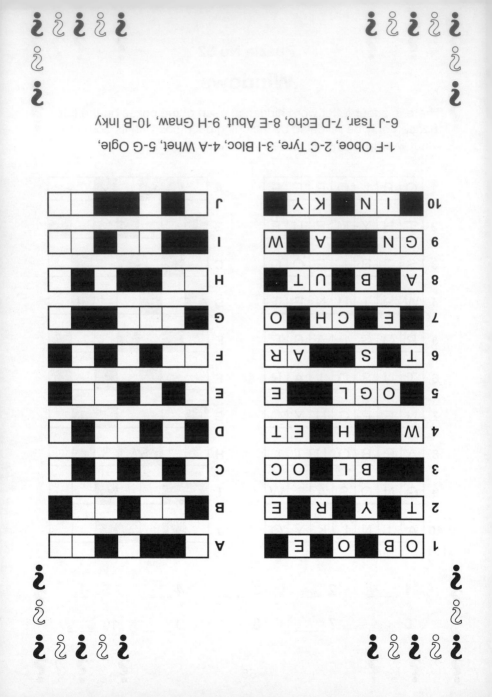

1-F Oboe, 2-C Tyre, 3-I Bloc, 4-A Whet, 5-G Ogle,
6-J Tsar, 7-D Echo, 8-E Abut, 9-H Gnaw, 10-B Inky

In Sequence

Which of the four alternatives (A, B, C or D) should take the place of the empty box in the sequence below?

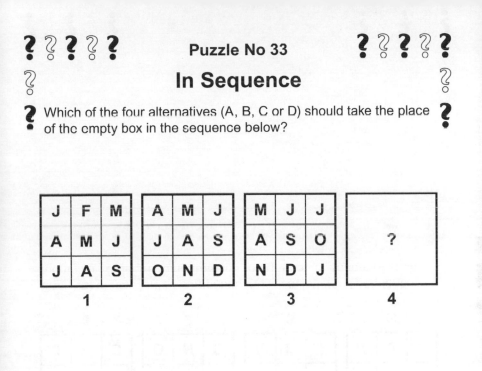

J	F	M
A	M	J
J	A	S

1

A	M	J
J	A	S
O	N	D

2

M	J	J
A	S	O
N	D	J

3

?

4

M	A	M
J	A	S
O	N	D

A

N	D	J
F	M	A
M	J	J

B

A	S	O
N	J	F
M	A	M

C

J	A	S
O	N	J
F	M	A

D

J	F	M		A	M	J		M	J	J		N	D	J
A	M	J		J	A	S		A	S	O		F	M	A
J	A	S		O	N	D		N	D	J		M	J	J
1				**2**				**3**				**B**		

Each set of nine letters comprises the initial letters of sequential months, in order, reading from left to right, top to bottom of each set.

Chaindoku

Fill each empty circle with a number from 1 to 6 inclusive.

Each row, each column and each set of linked circles should contain six different numbers.

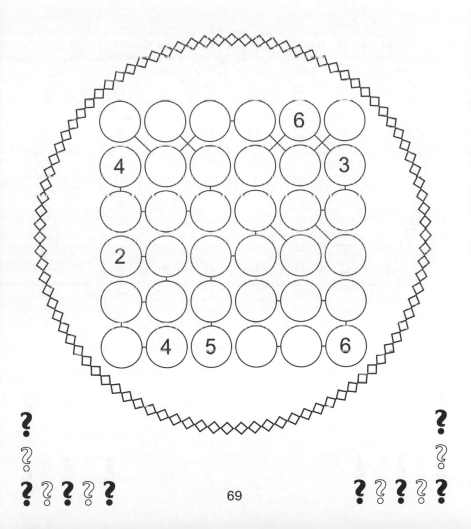

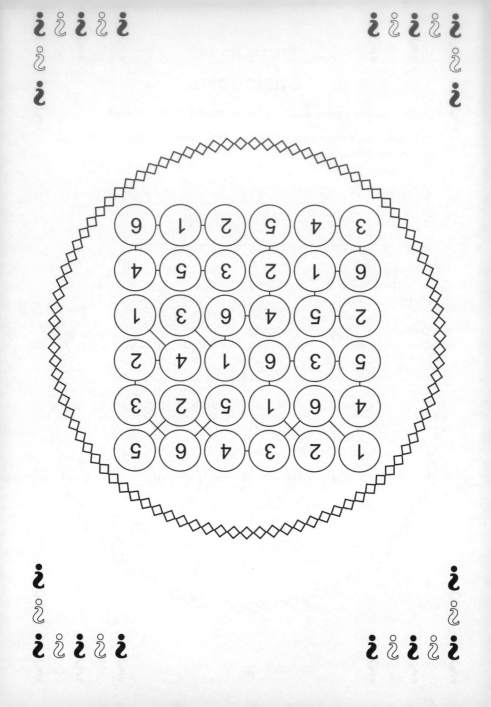

Logi-Nine

The numbers 1 to 9 inclusive should appear once in each row, as well as once in each column.

Every heavily outlined shape of nine smaller squares should also contain each of the numbers from 1 to 9.

Can you complete the grid?

	5	8		3		9	7	4
				4	6	1		
		4	1	2			5	
		2	7	5				8
3		1		7				
					4			
		7	8			5	3	
5	4	3		1	7	8		
2	1							

6	5	8	2	3	1	9	7	4
8	7	9	5	4	6	1	2	3
7	9	4	1	2	8	3	5	6
9	6	2	7	5	3	4	1	8
3	8	1	4	7	2	6	9	5
1	3	5	6	9	4	2	8	7
4	2	7	8	6	9	5	3	1
5	4	3	9	1	7	8	6	2
2	1	6	3	8	5	7	4	9

Word Ladders

In each of the word ladders below, change one letter at a time (but don't change the position of any letter) to make a new word – and move from the word at the top of the ladder to the word at the bottom using the exact number of rungs provided.

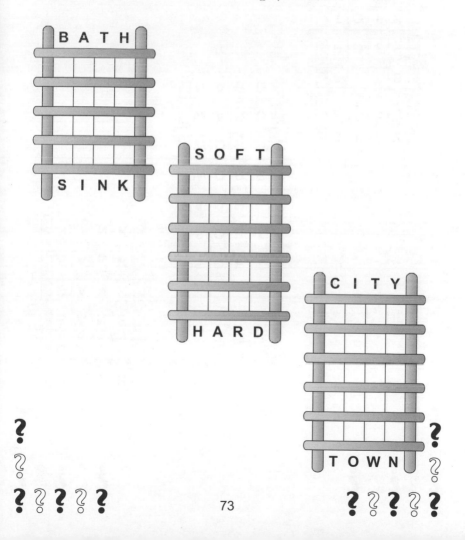

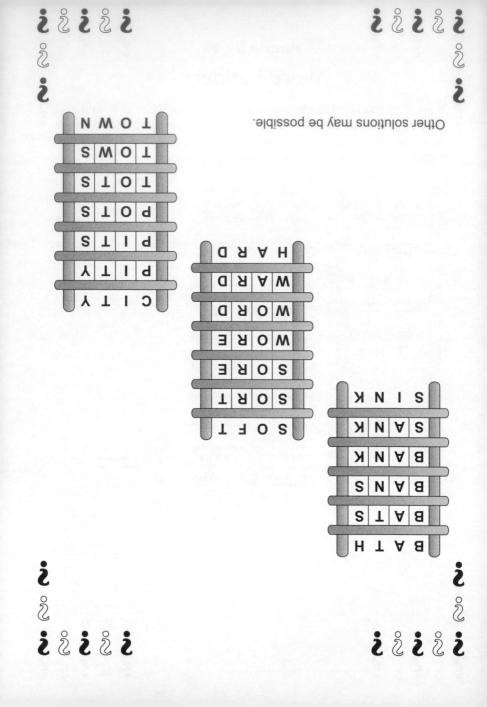

Other solutions may be possible.

T	O	W	N
T	O	W	S
T	O	T	S
P	O	T	S
P	I	T	S
P	I	T	Y
C	I	T	Y

H	A	R	D
W	A	R	D
W	O	R	D
W	O	R	E
S	O	R	E
S	O	R	T
S	O	F	T

S	I	N	K
S	A	N	K
B	A	N	K
B	A	N	S
B	A	T	S
B	A	T	H

Hexafit

Can you place the hexagons into the grid, so that where any hexagon touches another along a straight line, the contents of both triangles are the same? No rotation of any hexagon is allowed!

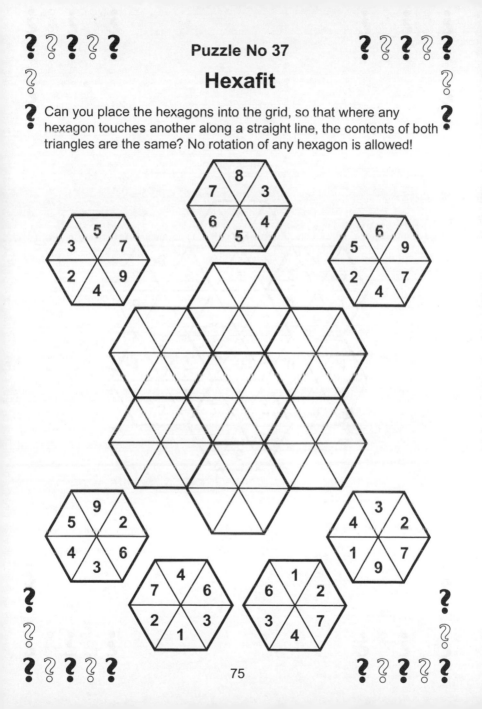

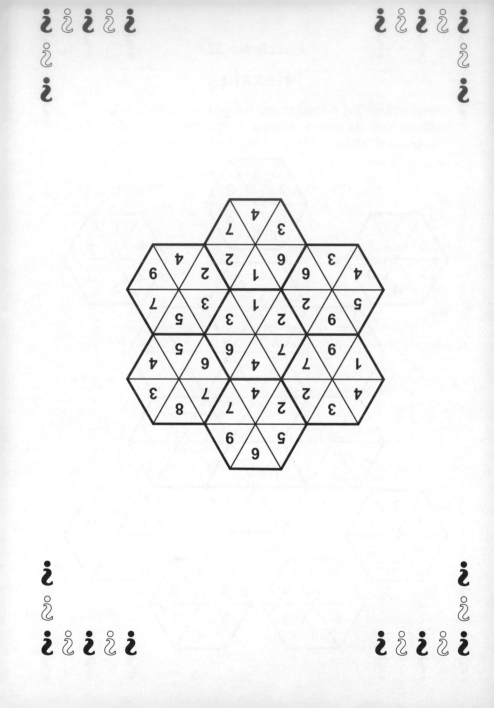

Coin Collecting

In this puzzle, an amateur coin collector has been out with his metal detector, searching for booty. He didn't have time to dig up all the coins he found, so has made a grid map, showing their locations, in the hope that if he loses the map, at least no one else will understand it... However, he didn't count on YOU coming across the strange grid (as seen here). Will you be able to discover the correct number of coins and their precise locations?

Those squares containing numbers are empty, but where a number appears in a square, it indicates how many coins are located in the squares (up to a maximum of eight) surrounding the numbered one, touching it at any corner or side. There is only one coin in any individual square. Place a circle into every square containing a coin.

		1	1	1			3			
1	3		3				3		0	
			3		2			1		
2		5	6		4	3	2			
	3								2	1
	4		4							2
3	4			2		2			4	4
			4			3		4		2
4			4			4	3	5		
2								5		2
	6		4	1			3		4	
				1					2	1

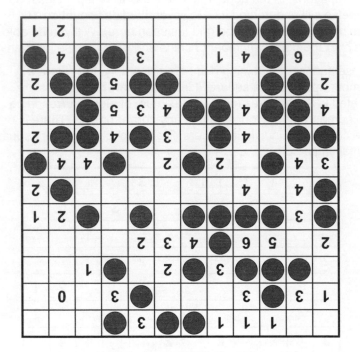

Puzzle No 39

Holesome Fun

In this puzzle, you must find an eight-letter word by deciding which common letter has been removed from the trios of words. Place that letter into the hole at the end of each row and the word will be revealed reading downwards.

_ U G E	T _ A T	E C _ O	◯
V _ S T	P E _ R	M _ I N	◯
_ I S P	N E _ T	_ A R P	◯
_ R A M	P A R _	_ A K E	◯
E A C _	C _ I N	S _ I P	◯
L O G _	_ V E R	I N T _	◯
F _ E E	A _ E A	H A _ M	◯
W I _ D	I _ C H	S _ O W	◯

(N) SNOW INCH WIND

(R) WARM AREA FREE

(O) INTO OVER LOGO

(H) SHIP CHIN EACH

(T) TAKE PART TRAM

(W) WARP NEWT WISP

(A) MAIN PEAR VAST

(H) ECHO THAT HUGE

Simple as ABC?

Each of the small squares in the grid below contains either A, B or C. Every row, column and each of the two long diagonals has exactly two of each letter. To help you solve this problem, we have provided as many clues as we think you will need! Can you tell the letter in each square?

ACROSS

1 The As are further left than the Bs.

2 No clue.

3 The Cs are further left than the Bs.

4 The As are further right than the Cs.

5 No clue.

6 The Bs are between the As.

DOWN

1 The Bs are higher than the As.

2 The Bs are lower than the Cs.

3 The Cs are lower than the Bs.

4 No clue.

5 The Bs are between the As.

6 The As are higher than the Cs.

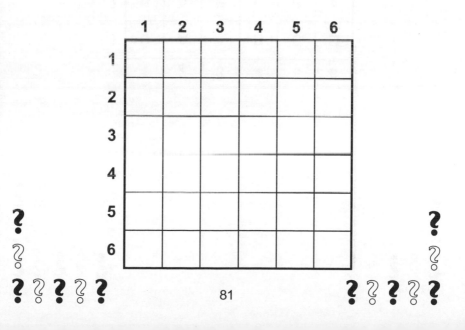

	1	2	3	4	5	6
1	C	A	A	B	C	B
2	B	A	B	C	C	A
3	C	C	B	A	A	B
4	B	C	C	A	B	A
5	A	B	A	C	B	C
6	A	B	C	B	A	C

Zigzag

The object of this puzzle is to trace a single path from the top left corner to the bottom right corner of the grid, travelling through all of the cells (tracking through the numbers in the sequence 1-2-3-4-5-6-7-8-1-2-3-4-5-6-7-8, etc) in either a horizontal, vertical or diagonal direction.

1	6	7	8	1	8	1	2
2	3	5	4	2	3	7	3
7	6	4	3	4	5	6	4
8	5	2	1	7	6	5	2
2	1	8	6	5	8	1	3
4	3	7	5	6	4	5	4
5	6	4	3	7	1	3	6
7	8	1	2	8	2	7	8

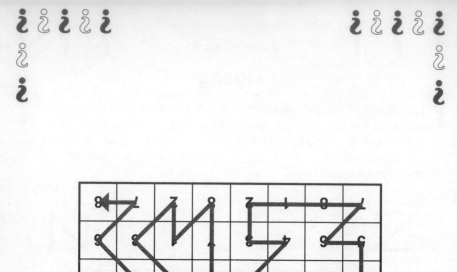
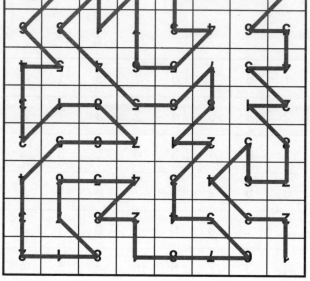

Total Concentration

The blank squares in this grid should be filled with whole numbers between 1 and 40 inclusive, any of which may occur more than once, or not at all.

The numbers in every horizontal row add up to the totals on the right, as do the two long diagonal lines; while those in every vertical column add up to the totals along the bottom.

Can you discover the missing numbers?

							153
39	15			21	38	13	159
	32		29	2		22	158
33	24	20	17		14		161
	17	24	26		20	25	152
40	3	23	12		1		142
16	30	34		19	25	30	183
11		4		36	18	27	163
167	148	170	158	167	141	167	204

							153
39	15	28	5	21	38	13	159
17	32	37	29	2	19	22	158
33	24	20	17	31	14	22	161
11	17	24	26	23	26	25	152
40	3	23	12	35	1	28	142
16	30	34	29	19	25	30	183
11	27	4	40	36	18	27	163
167	148	170	158	167	141	167	204

Round Dozen

First solve the clues. All of the solutions begin with the letter in the centre of the circle. When the puzzle is complete, you can then go on to discover the 12-letter word reading clockwise around the outermost ring of letters.

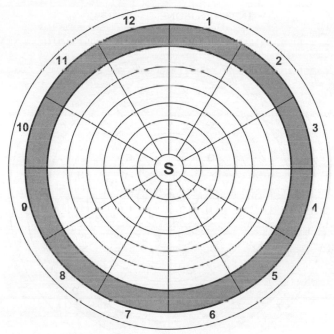

1 Divide, split up
2 Answer
3 Deriving pleasure from inflicting pain on another
4 Person unknown to you
5 Picturesque city of southern California (3,5)
6 Country, capital Ljubljana

7 Particular, clearly defined or identified
8 Two slices of bread with a filling between them
9 Band of colours, as seen in a rainbow
10 Portable travelling bag
11 Full set of bones
12 Most diminutive

The answer is: ENCROACHMENT

Wordfit

Can you fit all of the listed words into the grid below? One letter is already in place, to get you off to a good start.

3 Letters
SKI
TAG

4 Letters
DATA
GOAT
ICED
NORM
RIDE
ROUT
SKIM
SPIT
STUB
THEE

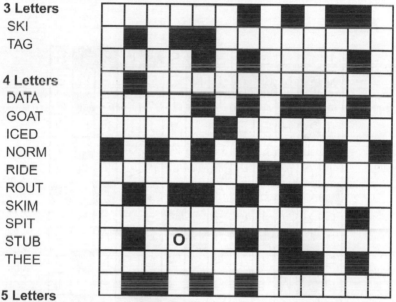

5 Letters

GAMUT	INDEED	LEOTARD
OMAHA	MARINE	PERSONA
ROUGE	PAMPER	
STEEL	PEARLS	**8 Letters**
THERE	PRIEST	EMERGENT
UNITE	TALENT	TEASPOON
	TRADER	

6 Letters
AVENUE
DEBRIS
EFFECT

7 Letters
HASSLED
INMATES

11 Letters
MOUNTAINEER
NECESSITATE

P	E	A	R	L	S	■	H	■	S	■	■	I
R	■	V	■	■	T	E	A	S	P	O	O	N
I	C	E	D	■	E	■	S	K	I	M	■	D
E	■	N	E	C	E	S	S	I	T	A	T	E
S	T	U	B	■	L	■	L	■	■	H	■	E
T	H	E	R	E	■	L	E	O	T	A	R	D
■	E	■	I	■	I	■	D	■	R	■	O	■
P	E	R	S	O	N	A	■	G	A	M	U	T
A	■	O	■	■	M	■	U	■	D	A	T	A
M	O	U	N	T	A	I	N	E	E	R	■	L
P	■	G	O	A	T	■	I	■	R	I	D	E
E	M	E	R	G	E	N	T	■	■	N	■	N
R	■	■	M	■	S	■	E	F	F	E	C	T

Well Spotted

Some of the circles in this puzzle are already black. Fill in more white circles, so that the number of black circles totals the number inside the area they surround.

Every black circle surrounding an area with a number higher than '1' needs to be next to another black circle surrounding the same area. When solving, it may help to put a small dot into any circle you know should not be filled.

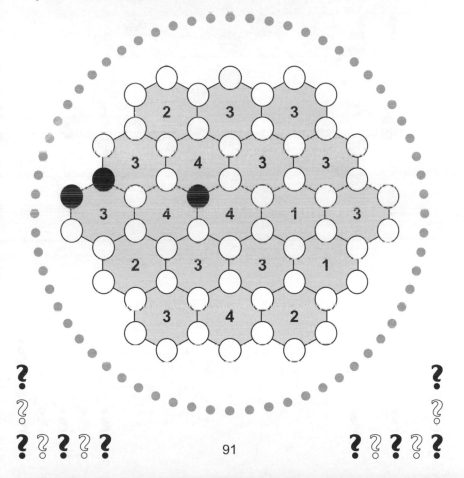

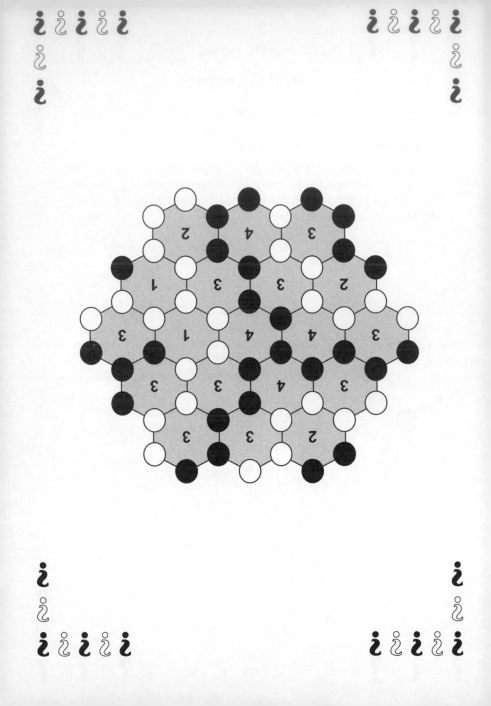

Alphafill

Place 25 different letters of the alphabet, one per circle, in order to spell out the listed words. Words are formed by moving between adjacent circles along the connecting lines, either horizontally, vertically or diagonally in any direction.

Begin by crossing out the letters already in place, together with the one letter that doesn't appear in any of the words.

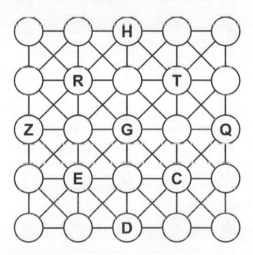

A B C D E F G H I J K L M
N O P Q R S T U V W X Y Z

BLAZED	JUT	RHYTHM	VIEW
FEAR	MORAL	SNUG	WARM
FIG	PEAR	STORM	YOGI
HOT	QUICK	STUCK	ZEAL

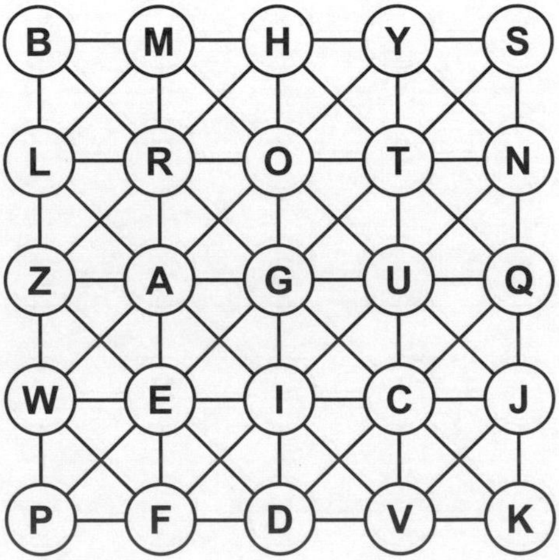

B M H Y S
L R O T N
Z A G U Q
W E I C J
P F D V K

Hoshi

The numbers 1 to 9 must be placed into the individual cells of each of the six large triangles.

No digit can appear more than once in any horizontal row or diagonal line of any length, even those rows and lines that are interrupted by the central hexagon.

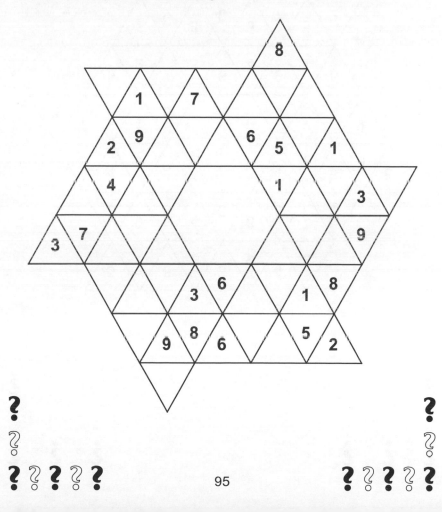

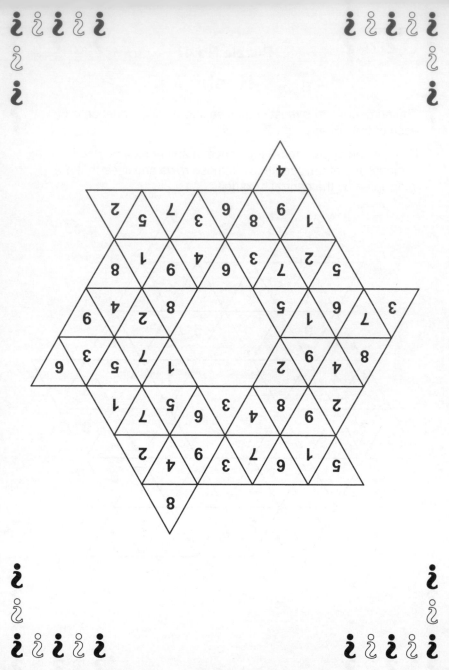

Pieceword

? This crossword has been cut into 24 pieces. Can you reassemble it by placing the remaining 20 pieces?

S Bend

Place the letters of each word, one per cell, so that every word flows in a clockwise direction around a number. Where the hexagons of one word overlap with those of another, the letter in each cell is common to both.

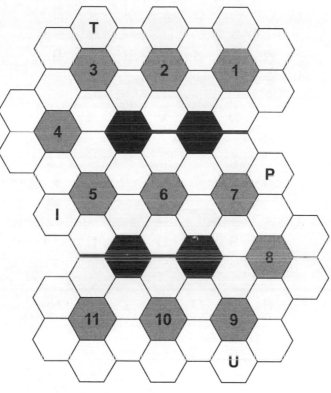

CICADA		PICNIC
COHORT	HAUNCH	QUORUM
DAMPEN	IMMUNE	ROCKET
EUREKA	ONRUSH	TRUANT

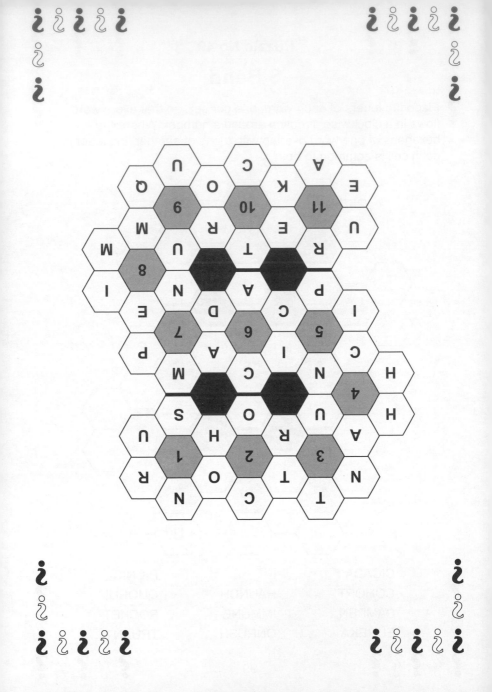

Loose Vowels

Every clue in this crossword consists of its solution, with the letters in order but minus its vowels. Your task is to replace the vowels; gd lck!

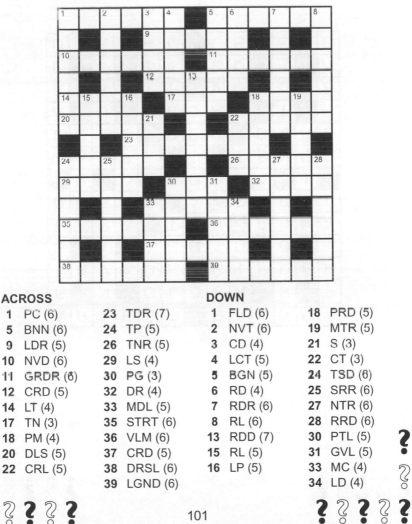

ACROSS

1	PC (6)
5	BNN (6)
9	LDR (5)
10	NVD (6)
11	GRDR (6)
12	CRD (5)
14	LT (4)
17	TN (3)
18	PM (4)
20	DLS (5)
22	CRL (5)

23	TDR (7)
24	TP (5)
26	TNR (5)
29	LS (4)
30	PG (3)
32	DR (4)
33	MDL (5)
35	STRT (6)
36	VLM (6)
37	CRD (5)
38	DRSL (6)
39	LGND (6)

DOWN

1	FLD (6)
2	NVT (6)
3	CD (4)
4	LCT (5)
5	BGN (5)
6	RD (4)
7	RDR (6)
8	RL (6)
13	RDD (7)
15	RL (5)
16	LP (5)

18	PRD (5)
19	MTR (5)
21	S (3)
22	CT (3)
24	TSD (6)
25	SRR (6)
27	NTR (6)
28	RRD (6)
30	PTL (5)
31	GVL (5)
33	MC (4)
34	LD (4)

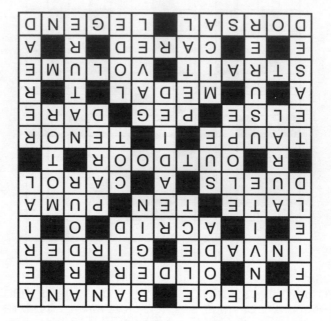

Skyscrapers

Place the numbers 1 to 7 into each row and column. Each number represents a skyscraper of that many floors. Organize the skyscrapers in such a way that the given number outside the grid represents the number of buildings which can be seen from that point, looking only at that number's row or column.

A skyscraper with a lower number of floors cannot hide a higher building, but one with a higher number of floors always hides any building behind it

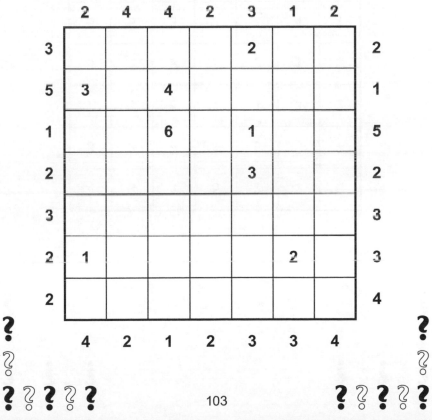

4	3	1	5	2	7	6
3	2	4	1	5	6	7
7	5	6	4	1	3	2
6	4	2	7	3	1	5
5	6	3	2	7	4	1
1	7	5	3	6	2	4
2	1	7	6	4	5	3

Number Cruncher

Just like a regular crossword, but with numbers as answers!

ACROSS

1 One eleventh of 17 Across (3)
4 11 Across minus 87 (3)
6 205 squared plus seven (5)
9 4 Down plus one sixth of 12 Across (2)
11 8 Down multiplied by six (3)
12 7 Down plus eight (2)
13 12 Across plus nine (2)
15 18 Across plus 8 Down minus one (2)
16 8 Down plus 19 Down plus 12 Across plus 10 Across (4)
17 16 Across plus 24 Across minus 292 (4)
18 4 Down plus 22 Down plus two (2)
20 15 Across plus one (2)
21 Months in four years (2)
22 11 Across plus 21 Across (3)
24 One eighth of 28 Across (2)
26 311 squared plus half of 28 Across (5)
28 2 Down multiplied by four (3)
29 1 Across minus two (3)

DOWN

1 29 Across plus 22 Down plus one (3)
2 Four cubed (2)
3 Ounces in nine stone (4)
4 Feet in four yards (2)
5 12 Across multiplied by 24 Across (3)
7 One twelfth of 22 Across (2)
8 Six squared (2)
10 21 Down multiplied by 179 (5)
12 188 squared minus 81 (5)
14 5 Down plus 7 Down minus two (3)
15 1 Down minus 134 (3)
19 Fathoms in 11 miles (4)
21 21 Across plus 22 Across plus 2 Down plus 8 Down (3)
22 One ninth of 25 Down (2)
23 7 Down multiplied by two (2)
25 13 Across multiplied by six (3)
26 Months in eight years (2)
27 One tenth of 14 Down (2)

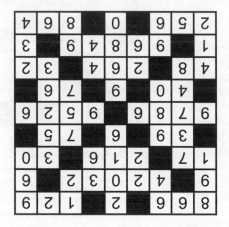

Round Numbers

Fill the circles so that every row and column of eight circles contains the numbers 1–8 inclusive. The shaded circles contain odd numbers 1, 3, 5 and 7, and the white circles contain even numbers 2, 4, 6 and 8. Some of the numbers are already in place.

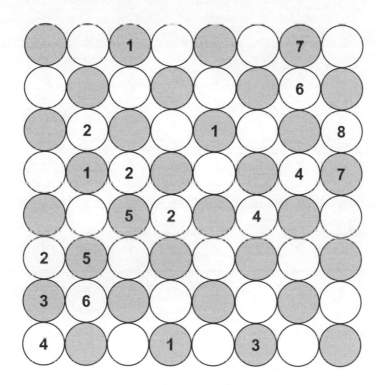

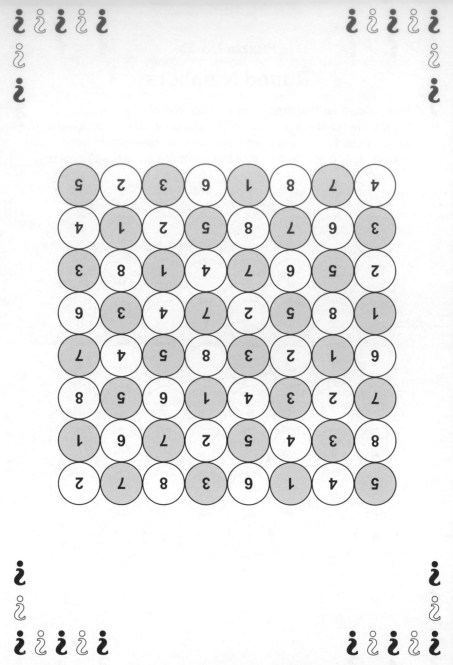

Combiku

Each horizontal row and vertical column should contain five different shapes and five different numbers. Every square will contain one number and one shape and no combination may be repeated anywhere else in the puzzle: for example, if a square has both a 4 and a star, then no other square will contain both a 4 and a star.

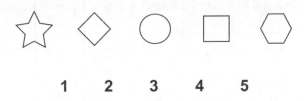

1   2   3   4   5

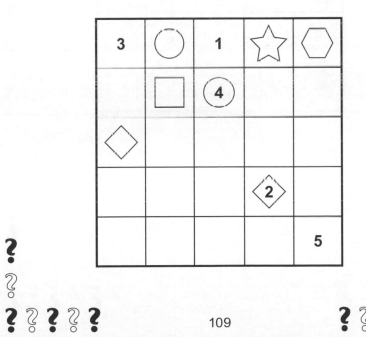

109

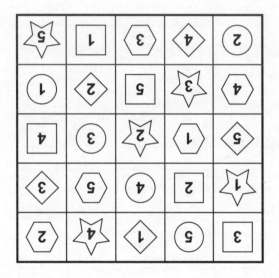

Latin Square

Fill the grid with numbers from 1 to 6, so that each number appears exactly once in every row and every column.

The clues refer to the sum of the numbers in the squares mentioned: for example, B C D 1 = 14 means that the numbers in squares B1, C1 and D1 add up to 14.

1 E F 4 = 8	5 A B C 1 = 11	9 F 1 2 = 8
2 A B 2 = 4	6 B 3 4 = 3	10 C 5 6 = 6
3 D 1 2 = 6	7 C D 3 = 9	11 D E 5 = 5
4 A 3 4 = 6	8 D E 6 = 6	12 C D E 4 = 15

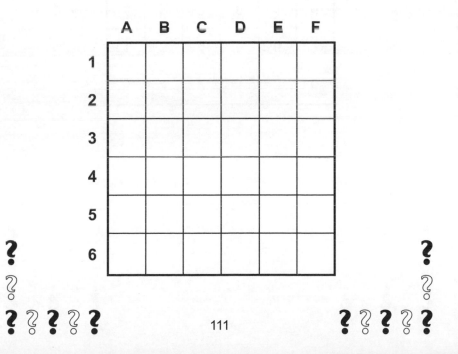

5	4	2	1	3	6
1	3	4	5	6	2
4	2	3	6	1	5
2	1	6	4	5	3
6	5	1	3	2	4
3	6	5	2	4	1

Battleships

Can you place the vessels into the diagram? Some parts of vessels or sea squares have already been filled in. A number to the left or above a row or column refers to the number of occupied squares in that row or column.

Any vessel may be positioned horizontally or vertically, but no part of a vessel touches part of any other vessel, either horizontally, vertically or diagonally.

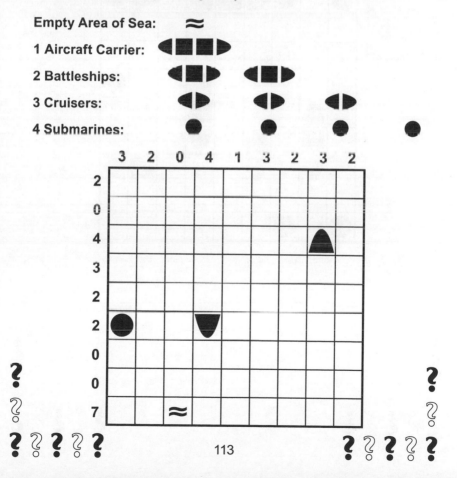

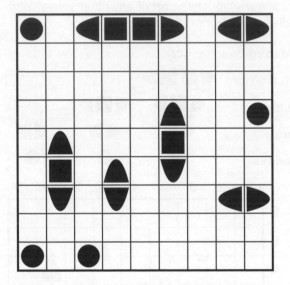

Arrowword

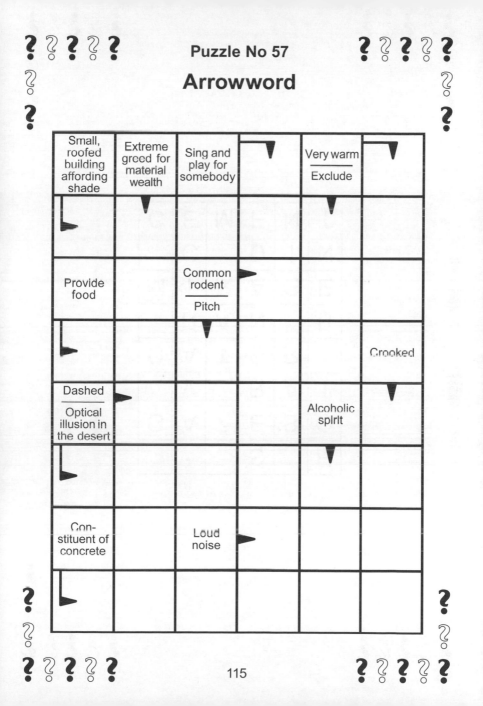

Small, roofed building affording shade	Extreme greed for material wealth	Sing and play for somebody	▼	Very warm ――― Exclude	▼
▼	▼			▼	
Provide food		Common rodent ――― Pitch	▶		
▼		▼			Crooked
Dashed ――― Optical illusion in the desert	▶			Alcoholic spirit	▼
▼				▼	
Con-stituent of concrete		Loud noise	▶		
▼					

			S		H
G	A	Z	E	B	O
	V		R	A	T
C	A	T	E	R	
	R	A	N		B
M	I	R	A	G	E
	C		D	I	N
C	E	M	E	N	T

Shape Up

Every row and column in this grid originally contained one circle, one diamond, one square, one triangle and two blank squares, although not necessarily in that order.

Every symbol with a black arrow refers to the first of the four symbols encountered when travelling in the direction of the arrow. Every symbol with a white arrow refers to the second of the four symbols encountered in the direction of the arrow.

Can you complete the original grid?

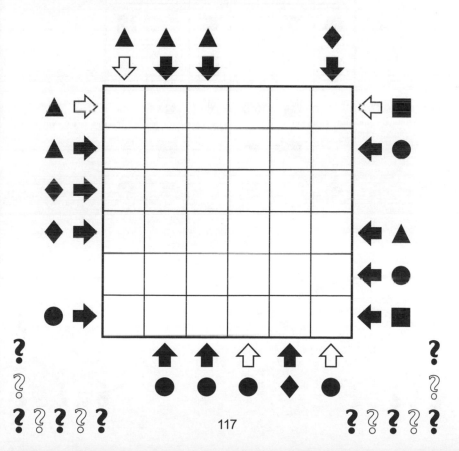

■	◆	▼	●		
●	▼		◆		■
▼			■	●	◆
	■	●	▼	◆	
	●	◆		■	▼
◆		■		▼	●

Puzzle No 59

Domino Placement

A standard set of 28 dominoes has been laid out as shown. Can you draw in the edges of them all? The check-box is provided as an aid and the domino already placed may help.

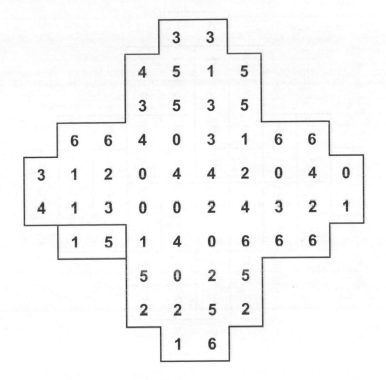

0-0	0-1	0-2	0-3	0-4	0-5	0-6	1-1	1-2	1-3	1-4	1-5	1-6	2-2
											✔		

2-3	2-4	2-5	2-6	3-3	3-4	3-5	3-6	4-4	4-5	4-6	5-5	5-6	6-6

A number/domino grid puzzle (digits printed rotated 180°):

```
              6  1
         2  5  2  2
         5  2  0  5
   6  6  6  0  4  1  5  1
1  2  3  4  2  0  0  3  1  4  3
0  4  0  2  4  4  0  2  1
   6  6  1  3  0  4  6  6
      5  3  5  3
      5  1  5  4
         3  3
```

Codeword

Every letter in this crossword has been replaced by a number, the number remaining the same for that letter wherever it occurs in the grid. Can you substitute numbers for letters and complete the crossword? It may help to cross off the letters either side of the grid to keep track of progress, and the reference box showing which numbers have been decoded can also aid solving. Three letters have already been entered into the grid, to help you on your way.

	1	2	3	4	5	6	7	8	9	10	11	12	13	
A	7	20	14	21	15	12	■	14	17	2	6	3	26	N
B	16	■	17	■	16	■	3	■	21	■	1	■	3	O
C	25	2	21	3	2	■	12	13	3	8	21	6	2	P
D	25	■	2	■	14	7	3	■	2	■	13	■	23	Q
E	14	7	2	6	6	■	7	13	3	17	6	3	16	R
F	■	■	16	■	2	■	6	■	9	■	■	21		S
G	10	6	7	9	22	2	■	6	18	6	8	17	14	T
H	6	■	■	16	■	■	16	■	3	■	3			U
I	3	2	26	24	3	15	11	■	22	20	16	15	12	V
J	13	■	20	■	5	■	11	6	5	■	17	■	3	W
K	20	16	17	2 (R)	3 (A)	12 (G)	6	■	3	13	21	3	14	X
L	16	■	20	■	19	■	2	■	13	■	20	■	14	Y
M	14	16	2	4	6	22	■	14	19	21	15	15	22	Z

1	2 R	3 A	4	5	6	7	8	9	10	11	12 G	13
14	15	16	17	18	19	20	21	22	23	24	25	26

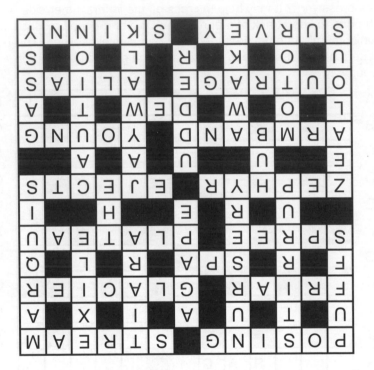

Calcudoku

Each row and column should contain the numbers 1–6. The numbers placed in a heavily outlined set of squares may be repeated, but must produce the calculation in the top left corner, using the mathematical symbol provided. So, for example, when multiplied, the numbers 3 and 4 total 12:

x12	
4	3

Any block of one square will contain the number in the top left corner.

x24		−1	x18	x15	+6
+5					
/4		/2			x30
+6			x40		
+11		+9		/2	
			+7		

4	6	5	3	1	2
2	3	6	1	5	4
1	4	2	6	3	5
3	1	4	5	2	6
5	2	1	4	6	3
6	5	3	2	4	1

Piecework

Place all of the pieces into the grid. Any may be rotated or flipped over, but none may touch another, not even diagonally at a corner.

The numbers outside the grid refer to the number of consecutive black squares; and each block is separated from the others by at least one white square. For instance, '3 2' could refer to a row with either none or any number of white squares, then three black squares, then at least one white square, then two more black squares, followed by either none or any number of white squares.

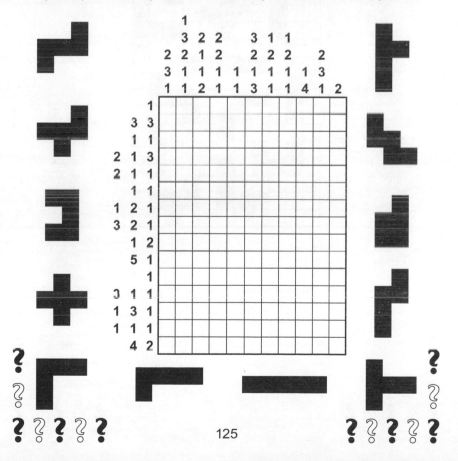

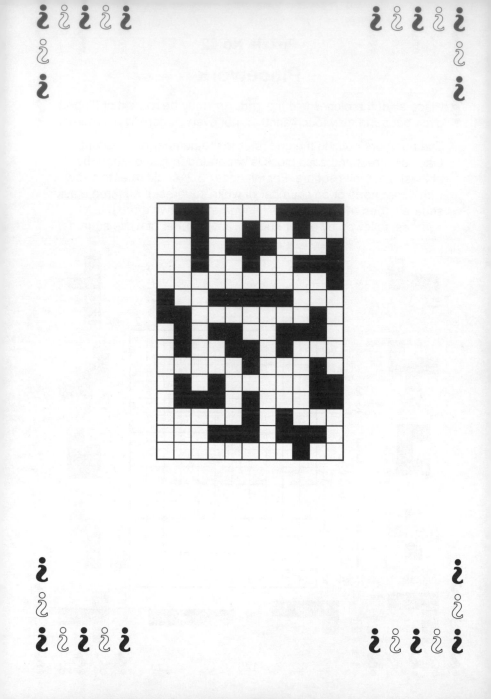

Tile Twister

Place the eight tiles into the puzzle grid so that all adjacent numbers on each tile match up. Tiles may be rotated through 360 degrees, but none may be flipped over.

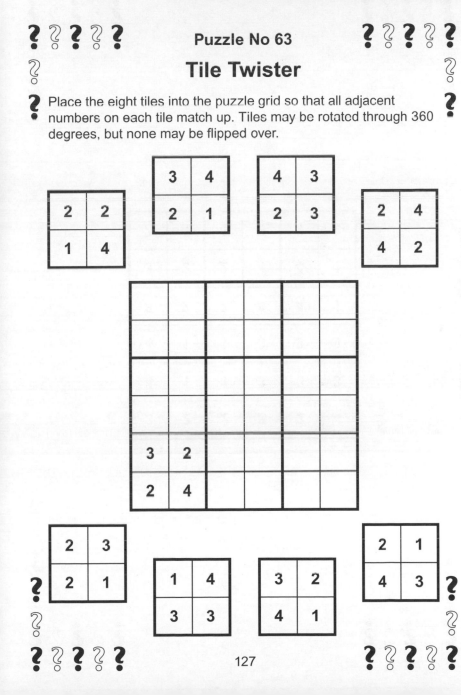

3	2	2	2	2	4
4	1	1	3	3	3
4	1	1	3	3	3
3	2	2	4	4	1
3	2	2	4	4	1
2	4	4	2	2	2

Box Clever

When the shape below is folded to form a cube, just one of the lettered alternatives can be produced. Which?

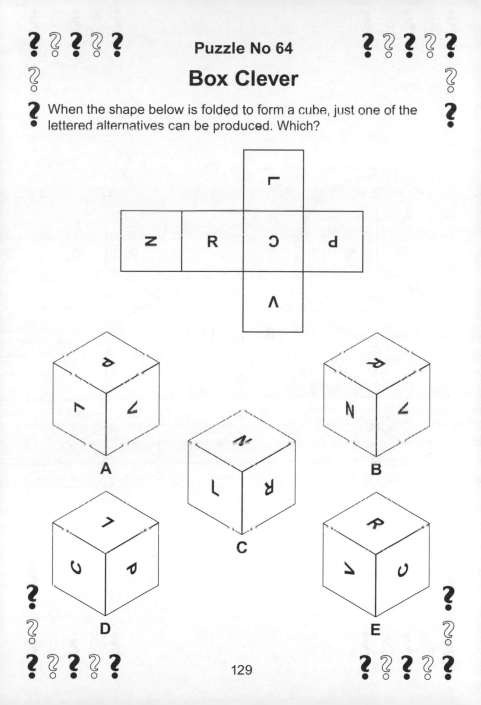

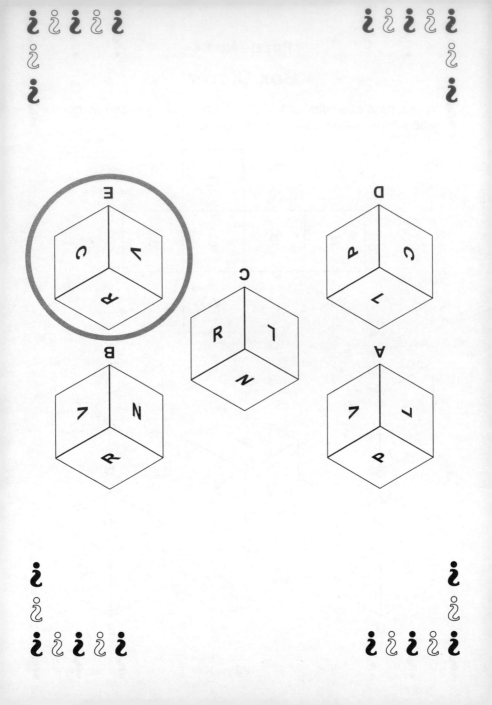

Three for One

? Find the word that links each of the three words in the clue. ?

ACROSS

1 Hard • Knife • Big (6)
4 Last • Poll • Short (5)
8 Out • Home • Desk (4)
9 Man • Sea • Flush (8)
11 Net • Snow • Wood (5)
12 Line • Due • Stamp (4)
15 Claim • Egg • Down (6)
17 Dress • Round • Full (6)
21 For • Price • Jumble (4)
24 Way • Bowling • Cat (5)
26 Group • Lose • Rate (8)
27 Fruit • Rock • Jump (4)
28 Forced • Hare • Past (5)
29 Tone • Strained • In (6)

DOWN

2 On • Camp • Bank (7)
3 Agent • Real • Car (6)
4 Out • Witness • For (5)
5 Angle • Just • Wing (5)
6 Done • Child • Part (4)
7 Wolf • Stop • Penny (7)
10 Away • Plus • Over (4)
13 Force • Dead • Mass (3)
14 Beyond • Up • Tape (7)
16 Health • Bode • Humour (3)
18 Time • Bone • Talk (4)
19 Lead • Gazing • Clear (7)
20 Demand • King's • Money (6)
22 Take • Hours • Ever (5)
23 Mother • Planet • Nut (5)
25 Feature • Set • Cling (4)

Light Up

Place circles (representing light bulbs) in some of the empty squares, in such a way that no two bulbs shine on each other, until every square of the grid is lit up. A bulb sends rays of light horizontally and vertically, illuminating its entire row and column unless its light is blocked by a black cell.

Some black cells contain numbers, indicating how many light bulbs are in adjacent squares either immediately above, below, to the right or to the left. Bulbs placed diagonally adjacent to a numbered cell do not contribute to the bulb count. An unnumbered black cell may have any number of light bulbs adjacent to it, or none at all, and not all light bulbs are necessarily clued via black squares.

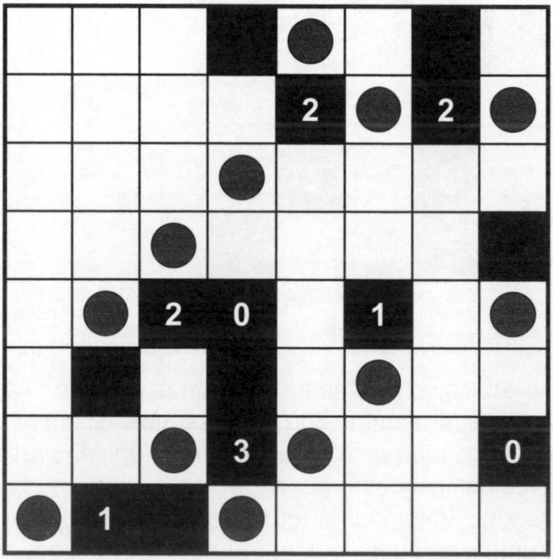

Kakuro

Using single digits from 1 to 9 inclusive, fill the grid so that the numbers in each block add up to the total in the box above or to the left of it. No digit may be used twice in a block. The same digit may occur more than once in a row or column, but it must be in a separate block.

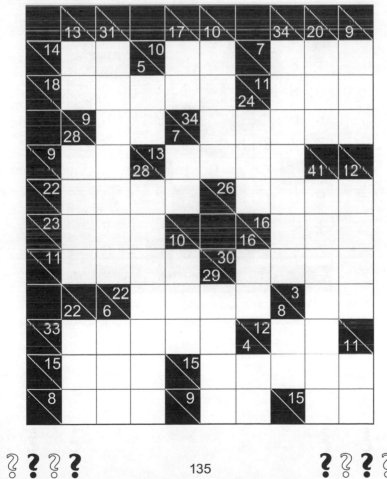

9	5		9	1		1	4	2
4	1	3	8	2		3	7	1
	7	2		4	8	7	9	6
6	3		1	3	7	2		
9	4	3	6		9	8	7	2
8	9	6				4	9	3
5	2	1	3		7	9	8	6
		5	1	7	9		2	1
8	3	7	6	9		7	5	
9	2	4		5	3	1	4	2
5	1	2		8	1		6	9

Slitherlink

Draw a single continuous loop, by connecting the dots. No line may cross the path of another.

The figure inside each set of any four surrounding dots indicates the total number of surrounding lines.

```
.   .   .   .   .   .   .   .   .   .   .   .
  3           3         2   3   2
.   .   .   .   .   .   .   .   .   .   .   .
    1       2       1       1   2   3
.   .   .   .   .   .   .   .   .   .   .   .
  3           3       2               2
.   .   .   .   .   .   .   .   .   .   .   .
  3   0   1           2   2   1   2
.   .   .   .   .   .   .   .   .   .   .   .
          3   1       2               2
.   .   .   .   .   .   .   .   .   .   .   .
      1   2   3   2   1   2   0   2
.   .   .   .   .   .   .   .   .   .   .   .
  2       2                   2
.   .   .   .   .   .   .   .   .   .   .   .
      2       3       3       2   1
.   .   .   .   .   .   .   .   .   .   .   .
  1   0           3   2   1       2   2
.   .   .   .   .   .   .   .   .   .   .   .
              2       1
.   .   .   .   .   .   .   .   .   .   .   .
  2   3   1       2       2   1   0
.   .   .   .   .   .   .   .   .   .   .   .
              2       2   2           3
.   .   .   .   .   .   .   .   .   .   .   .
  1       0   0   2   2   3       1
.   .   .   .   .   .   .   .   .   .   .   .
```

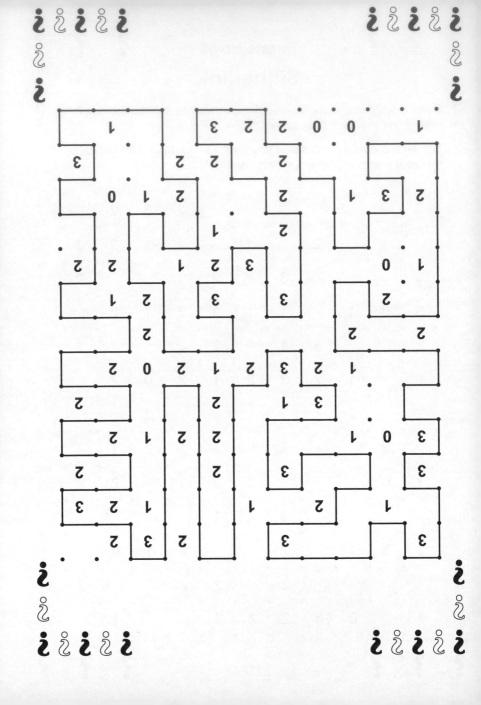

Egg Timer

Can you complete this puzzle in the time that it takes to boil an egg? The answers to the clues are anagrams of the words immediately above and below, plus or minus a letter.

1 Wades in shallow water

2 Out of date

3 Digging tool

4 Recess at the east end of a church

5 Intervening distance between places

6 Get away, break free

7 Common soft fruits

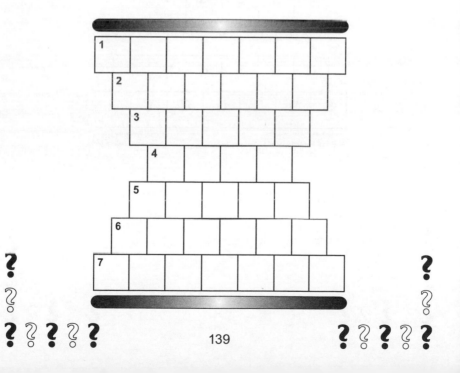

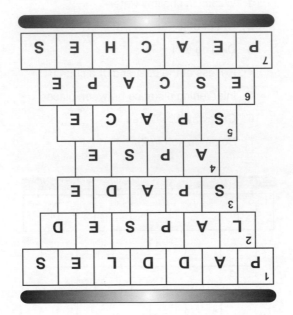

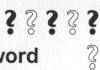

General Knowledge Crossword

ACROSS

3 Scottish loch (6)

6 Spanish form of address for a married woman (6)

7 Woman whose dancing beguiled Herod into giving her the head of John the Baptist (6)

10 Capital of Greece (6)

11 Deciduous conifer (5)

14 Prince who abducted Helen of Troy (5)

18 Sour-tasting (6)

19 Capital of Northern Territory, Australia (6)

21 Greek goddess of wisdom (6)

22 Warm-blooded creature (6)

DOWN

1 Country, capital Jerusalem (6)

2 Item that prevents a ship from moving (6)

3 Long noosed rope used to catch animals (5)

4 Yoko ____, widow of John Lennon (3)

5 Mature female deer (3)

8 Tibetan or Mongolian priest (4)

9 African republic, capital Damako (4)

12 City, site of the Taj Mahal (4)

13 Black bird with a raucous call (4)

15 Arm of the Indian Ocean between Africa and Arabia (3,3)

16 Marked by friendly companionship with others (6)

17 Narrow waterway used by barges (5)

19 Barrier that contains the flow of water (3)

20 Cane spirit (3)

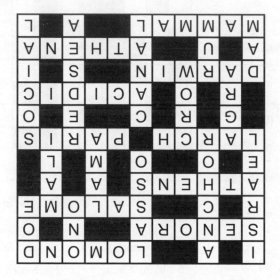

Puzzle No 71

Around the Block

You won't need a starting block to get you under way, because it isn't a race! Just arrange the six-letter solutions to the clues into the six blocks around each clue number.

Write the answers in a clockwise or anticlockwise direction and you'll find that the last answer fits into the first; the problem is to decide in which square to put the first letter of each word…

1 Body orbiting a star

2 Relating to the mountains

3 Turn inside out

4 Watchman, guard

5 Indigenous person

6 Go round and round

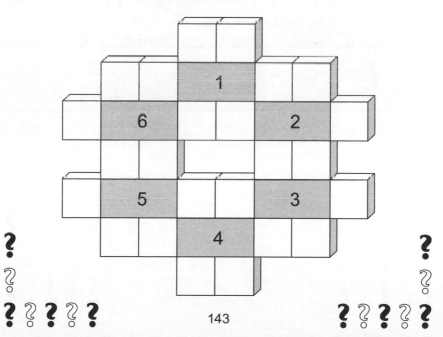

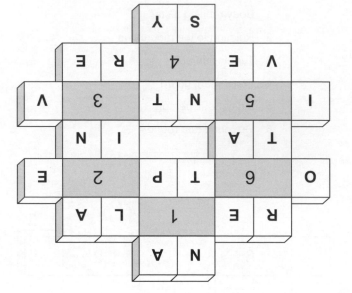

Around the Clock

Puzzle No

1 Planet (a/c), 2 Alpine (a/c), 3 Invert (c),
4 Sentry (c), 5 Native (a/c), 6 Rotate (a/c)

? ? ? ? ?

Puzzle No 72

? ? ? ? ?

Eliminator

Every oval shape contains a different letter of the alphabet from A to K inclusive. Use the clues to determine their locations. Reference in the clues to 'due' means in any location along the same horizontal or vertical line.

1 B is due west of A, which is due south of K.

2 C is due north of J, which is due west of K.

3 D is due south of H, which is due west of B.

4 I is due east of G, which is due north of E.

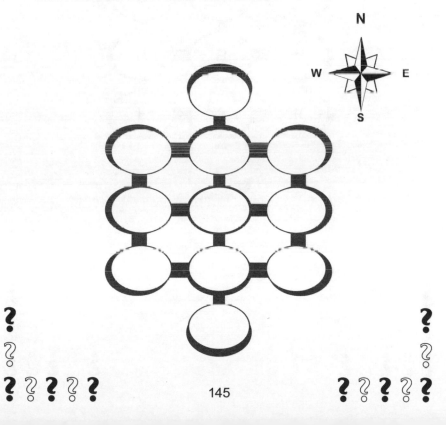

145

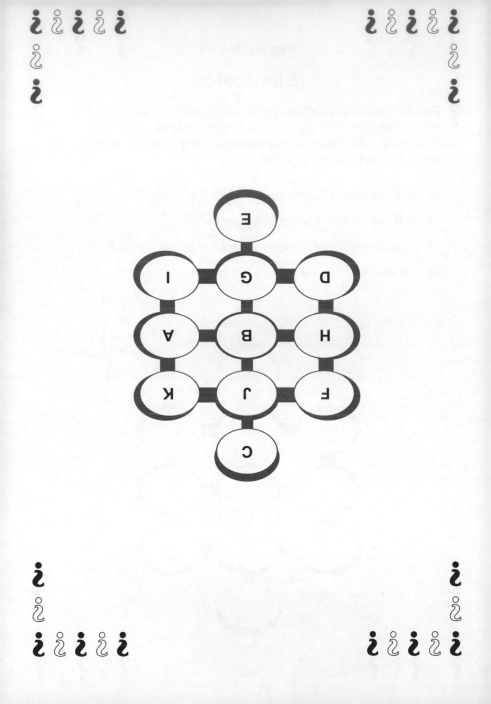

Figure It Out

Every square in the grid is to be filled with a single digit number from 1 to 9 – each of those numbers being used four times. Use the clues to complete the grid, bearing in mind that the same number must not appear in two adjacent (touching) squares either across or down. If the same number is used more than once in any row across or column down, it is stated in the relevant clue.

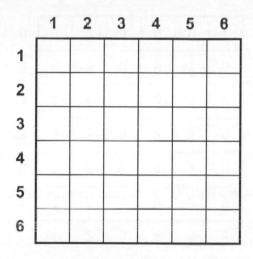

ACROSS

1. Two *nines*. No *three*. *Eight* is the only even number.
2. Two *sixes* are the highest numbers.
3. Total twenty-one.
4. Consecutive numbers placed in order.
5. No *four*.
6. Two *sevens*.

DOWN

1. Two *ones*.
2. Consecutive numbers placed in order.
3. Two *fives*. *Six* is the highest number.
4. Two *nines* are the only odd numbers.
5. Two *ones*. *Eight* is the only even number
6. Total thirty-nine.

	1	2	3	4	5	6
1	1	7	5	9	8	9
2	2	6	3	4	1	6
3	1	5	6	2	3	4
4	3	4	5	6	7	8
5	8	3	2	9	1	5
6	7	2	4	8	9	7

Round Up

The number in each circle is the sum of the two numbers below it. Just work out the missing numbers in every circle!

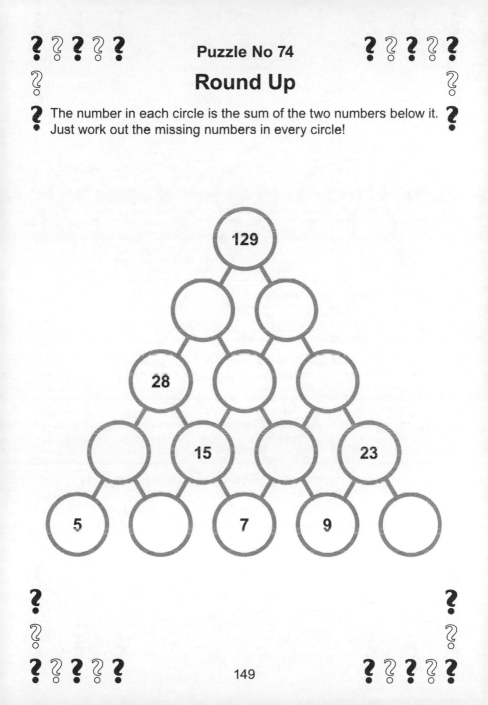

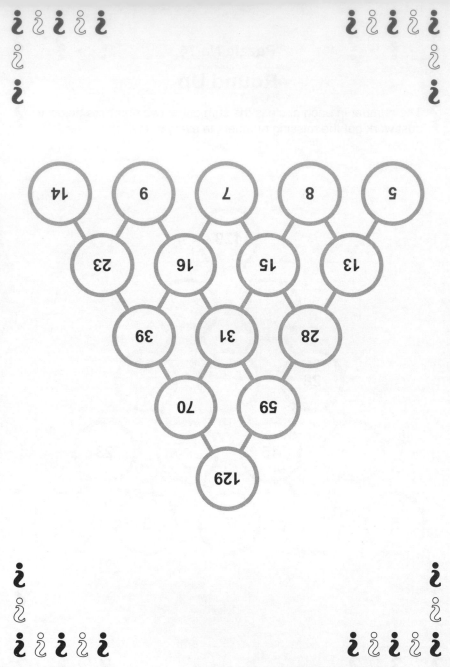

Windows

There is a four-letter word hidden in each of the boxes on the left that can only be revealed by matching each box with its correct window-strip on the right. Can you match all ten?

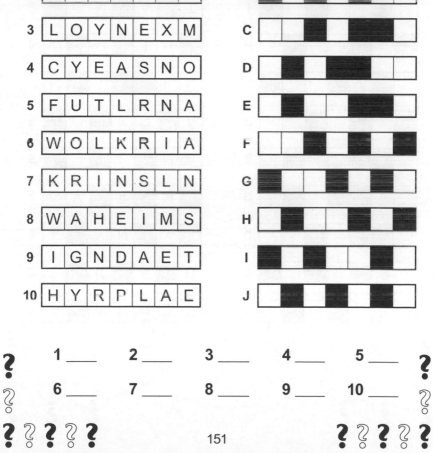

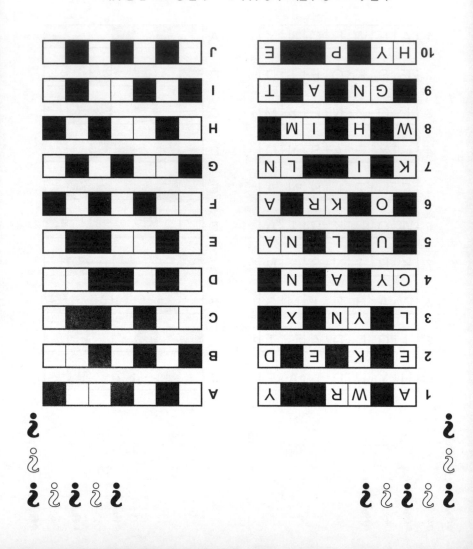

1-E Awry, 2-J Eked, 3-H Lynx, 4-F Cyan, 5-B Ulna,
6-I Okra, 7-D Kiln, 8-A Whim, 9-G Gnat, 10-C Hype

In Sequence

Which of the four alternatives (A, B, C or D) should take the place of the empty box in the sequence below?

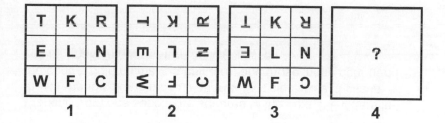

1 2 3 4

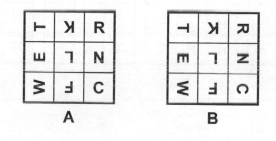

A B

C D

T	K	R
E	L	N
W	F	C

1

⊣	Ʞ	ᴚ
ᴍ	⅂	Z
M	⅃	ᴄ

2

⊥	K	ᴚ
Ǝ	L	N
M	F	ᴄ

3

⊢	K	ᴚ
E	⅃	N
M	ⅎ	ᴄ

D

Working from one set of nine squares to the next, the letters in the left-hand column make a quarter turn clockwise, those in the central column make a half turn, and those in the right-hand column make a quarter turn anticlockwise.

Chaindoku

Fill each empty circle with a number from 1 to 6 inclusive.

Each row, each column and each set of linked circles should contain six different numbers.

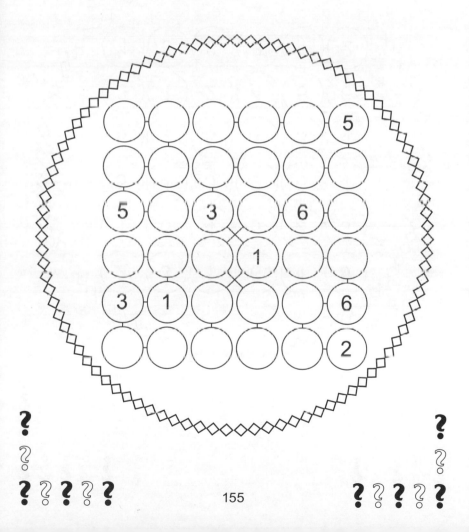

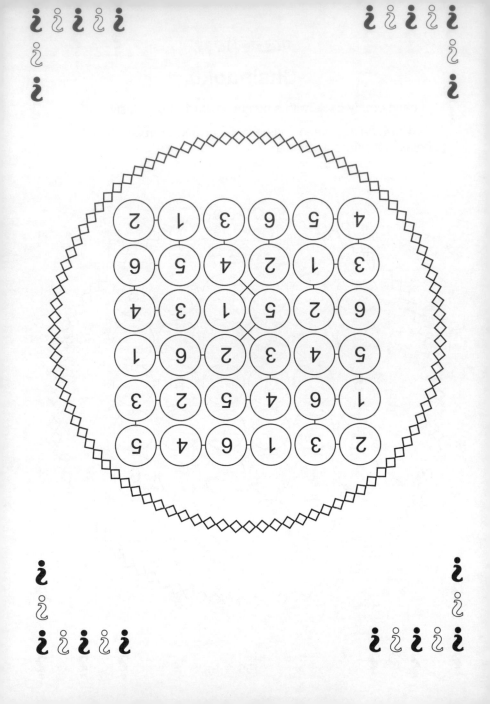

Logi-Nine

The numbers 1 to 9 inclusive should appear once in each row, as well as once in each column.

Every heavily outlined shape of nine smaller squares should also contain each of the numbers from 1 to 9.

Can you complete the grid?

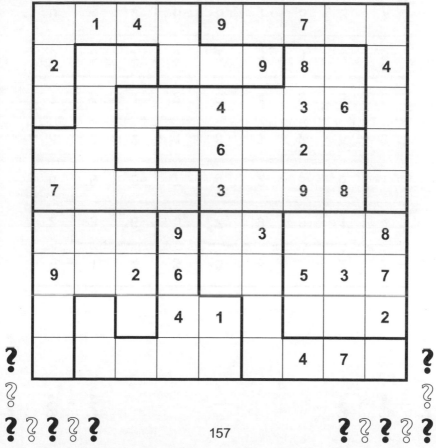

6	1	4	3	9	8	7	2	5
2	3	6	5	7	9	8	1	4
8	9	5	7	4	2	3	6	1
4	8	9	1	6	7	2	5	3
7	5	1	2	3	4	9	8	6
5	6	7	9	2	3	1	4	8
9	4	2	6	8	1	5	3	7
3	7	8	4	1	5	6	9	2
1	2	3	8	5	6	4	7	9

Word Ladders

In each of the word ladders below, change one letter at a time (but don't change the position of any letter) to make a new word – and move from the word at the top of the ladder to the word at the bottom using the exact number of rungs provided.

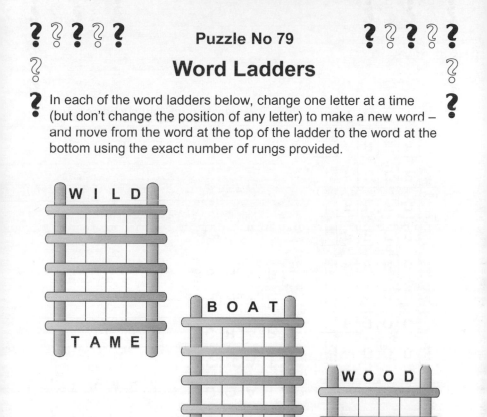

WILD
MILD
MILE
MALE
TALE
TAME

BOAT
COAT
CHAT
CHAP
CHIP
SHIP

WOOD
FOOD
FOND
FEND
FEED
FLED
FLEE
FREE
TREE

Other solutions may be possible.

Hexafit

Can you place the hexagons into the grid, so that where any hexagon touches another along a straight line, the contents of both triangles are the same? No rotation of any hexagon is allowed!

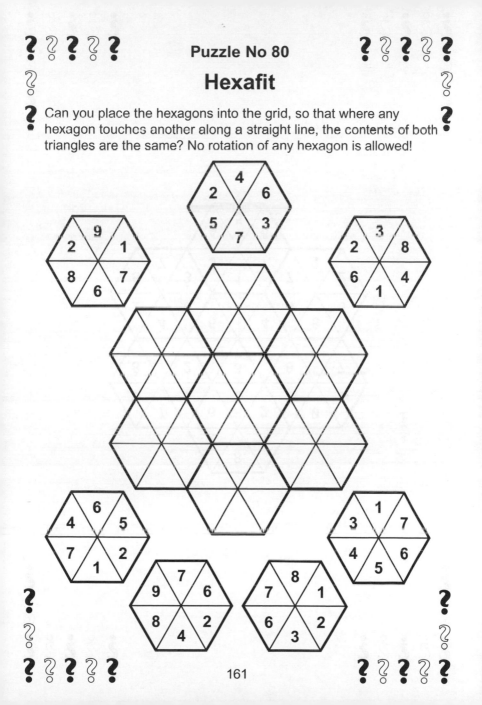

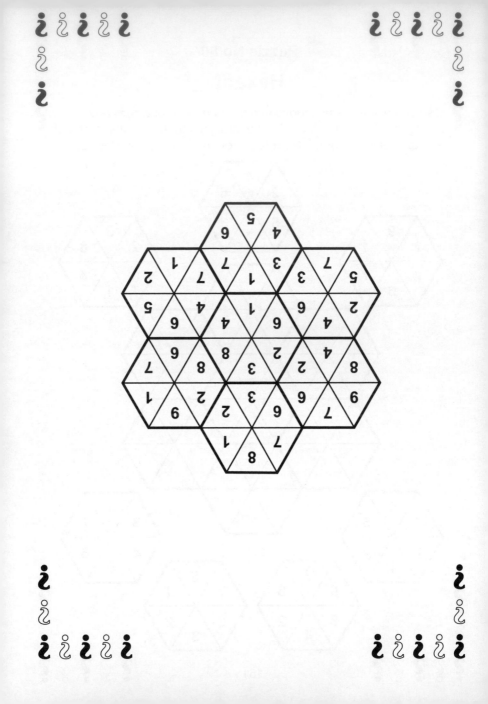

Coin Collecting

In this puzzle, an amateur coin collector has been out with his metal detector, searching for booty. He didn't have time to dig up all the coins he found, so has made a grid map, showing their locations, in the hope that if he loses the map, at least no one else will understand it... However, he didn't count on YOU coming across the strange grid (as seen here). Will you be able to discover the correct number of coins and their precise locations?

Those squares containing numbers are empty, but where a number appears in a square, it indicates how many coins are located in the squares (up to a maximum of eight) surrounding the numbered one, touching it at any corner or side. There is only one coin in any individual square. Place a circle into every square containing a coin.

1					1		1	1	3	
	2	1			0					
							1	3		
3	4		4		2	0		2		4
	3				2					2
	4		2	3		1		4		2
	1						2		2	
1				3			2		2	
	2			2		2	2			
	2		1	2		2				2
	1		2					4	3	1
		1		2	1	1				

Coin Collecting

		●	●		1	1	2	●	1	
1	3	4		●			●	2		1
2	●	●	2		2		1		2	●
●		2		2	●	2			●	2
	2		2	●		3	●			1
	2	●	2			●		1		●
2	●	4		1	●	●	3	2	●	4
2	●	●			2		●		3	●	●
	4		2		0	2	●	4	●	3
	●	3	1				●			●
●	●				0			2	1	●
●	3	1	1	●	1					1

Holesome Fun

In this puzzle, you must find an eight-letter word by deciding which common letter has been removed from the trios of words. Place that letter into the hole at the end of each row and the word will be revealed reading downwards.

_ A S T	A _ E N	C A _ E	◯
C _ R E	R O _ M	B _ O T	◯
_ E S T	P A _ T	_ O R M	◯
_ R G E	P E R _	_ G L Y	◯
C A _ P	E _ I T	O _ E N	◯
P A L _	_ R G O	P U R _	◯
S _ A P	K _ O W	P I _ K	◯
S I _ E	I _ C H	A _ O M	◯

(T)	ATOM	ITCH	SITE
(N)	PINK	KNOW	SNAP
(E)	PURE	ERGO	PALE
(M)	OMEN	EMIT	CAMP
(U)	UGLY	PERU	URGE
(N)	NORM	PANT	NEST
(O)	BOOT	ROOM	CORE
(M)	CAME	AMEN	MAST

Puzzle No 83

Simple as ABC?

Each of the small squares in the grid below contains either A, B or C. Every row, column and each of the two long diagonals has exactly two of each letter. To help you solve this problem, we have provided as many clues as we think you will need! Can you tell the letter in each square?

ACROSS

1 The Bs are further left than the As.
2 The As are between the Cs.
3 The Cs are between the Bs.
4 The Bs are between the Cs.
5 No clue.
6 No clue.

DOWN

1 The As are between the Cs.
2 Each A is directly next to and above a B.
3 The As are lower than the Cs.
4 The Bs are between the As.
5 No clue.
6 Each B is directly next to and below a C.

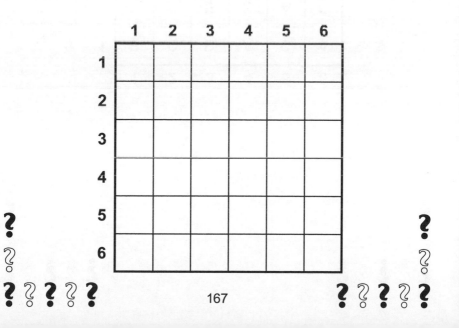

	1	2	3	4	5	6
1	B	C	B	A	C	A
2	C	A	B	B	A	C
3	A	B	C	C	A	B
4	A	A	C	B	B	C
5	C	B	A	A	C	B
6	B	C	A	C	B	A

Zigzag

The object of this puzzle is to trace a single path from the top left corner to the bottom right corner of the grid, travelling through all of the cells (tracking through the numbers in the sequence 1-2-3-4-5-6-7-8-1-2-3-4-5-6-7-8, etc) in either a horizontal, vertical or diagonal direction.

1	4	5	7	8	7	8	1
2	3	6	1	6	4	2	4
2	1	4	2	3	5	5	3
8	3	5	5	3	2	6	8
4	7	6	6	4	8	1	7
5	3	8	1	7	5	1	2
6	1	2	7	4	6	4	3
7	8	2	3	6	5	7	8

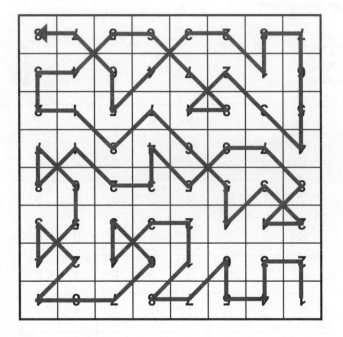

Total Concentration

The blank squares in this grid should be filled with whole numbers between 1 and 40 inclusive, any of which may occur more than once, or not at all.

The numbers in every horizontal row add up to the totals on the right, as do the two long diagonal lines; while those in every vertical column add up to the totals along the bottom.

Can you discover the missing numbers?

							157
8		19	12	4	17		122
35		30	21	36	15	7	145
20	34		10		23	11	151
17	13	31	1	3			124
		33	15	40	2	38	148
	16	5		22	28	18	123
26	23	11		32		39	154
117	126	153	97	166	131	177	141

							157
8	25	19	12	4	17	37	122
35	1	30	21	36	15	7	145
20	34	24	10	29	23	11	151
17	13	31	1	3	32	27	124
6	14	33	15	40	2	38	148
5	16	5	29	22	28	18	123
26	23	11	9	32	14	39	154
117	126	153	97	166	131	177	141

Round Dozen

First solve the clues. All of the solutions begin with the letter in the centre of the circle. When the puzzle is complete, you can then go on to discover the 12-letter word reading clockwise around the outermost ring of letters.

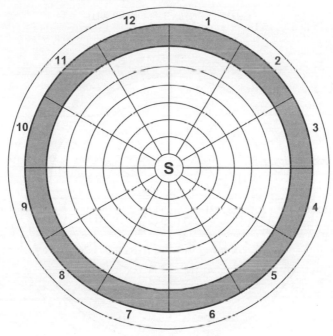

1. Country, capital Paramaribo
2. Highly contagious viral disease, also known as 'variola'
3. Directly, without a bend
4. Deepest of the Great Lakes
5. Mediterranean island to the west of Italy
6. White, early spring flower
7. Capital of Chile
8. Arboreal rodent with a long, bushy tail
9. Country, capital Colombo (3,5)
10. Deduct, take away
11. Period of time for which a criminal is imprisoned
12. Country of the UK

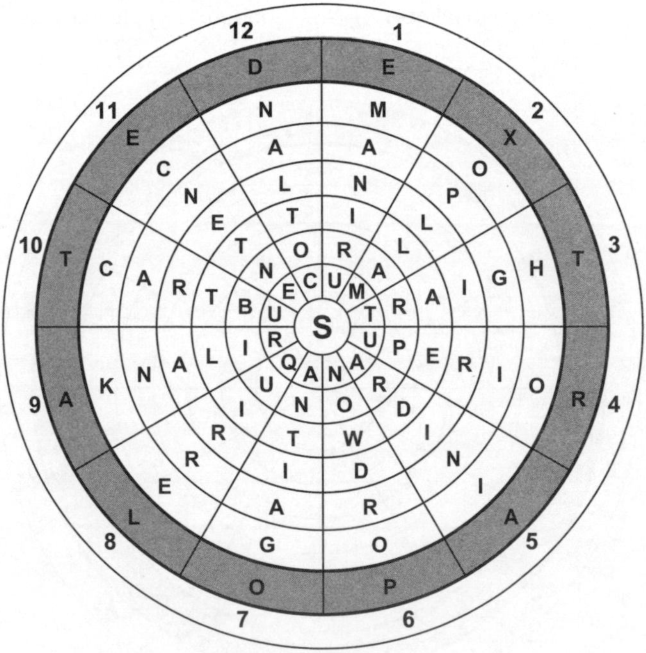

The answer is: EXTRAPOLATED

Wordfit

Can you fit all of the listed words into the grid below? One letter is already in place, to get you off to a good start.

3 Letters
AND
AXE
EAR
HER

4 Letters
ARCH
DILL
NINE
ROTA
SAGA
WAFT

5 Letters
AORTA
BISON
HALTS
KNEES
MODEL
PIXEL

6 Letters
BARIUM
FORCES
GARTER
LITMUS

7 Letters
BLOTTER
COAXING
FITTING
FURNACE
STEEPLE
WIDOWER

8 Letters
CHENILLE
ORIGINAL

9 Letters
EXCEPTION
EXPEDIENT

10 Letters
NASTURTIUM
REGENERATE

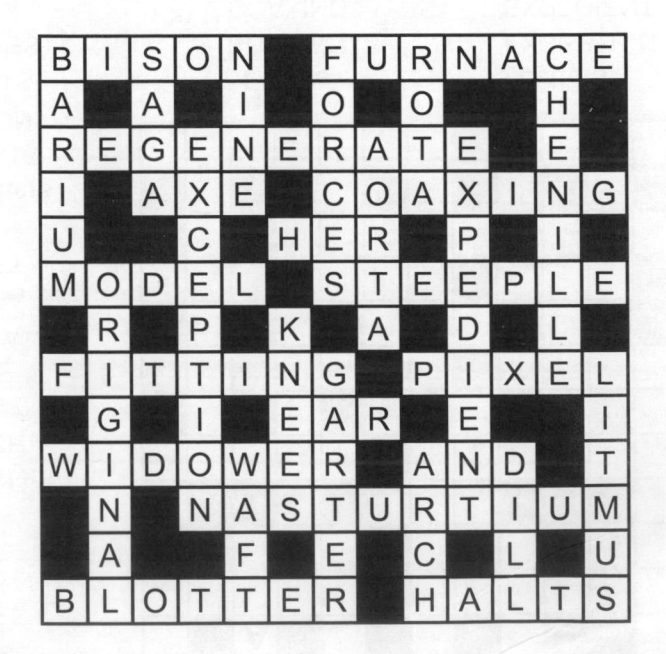

Well Spotted

Some of the circles in this puzzle are already black. Fill in more white circles, so that the number of black circles totals the number inside the area they surround.

Every black circle surrounding an area with a number higher than '1' needs to be next to another black circle surrounding the same area. When solving, it may help to put a small dot into any circle you know should not be filled.

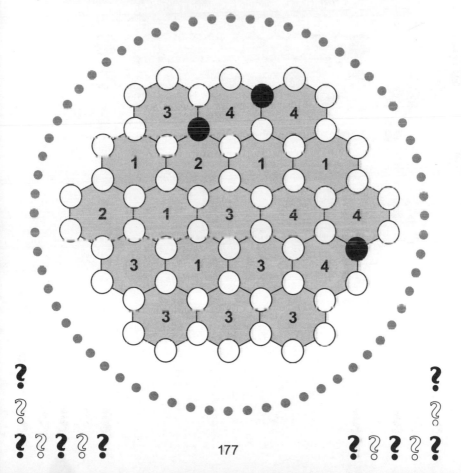

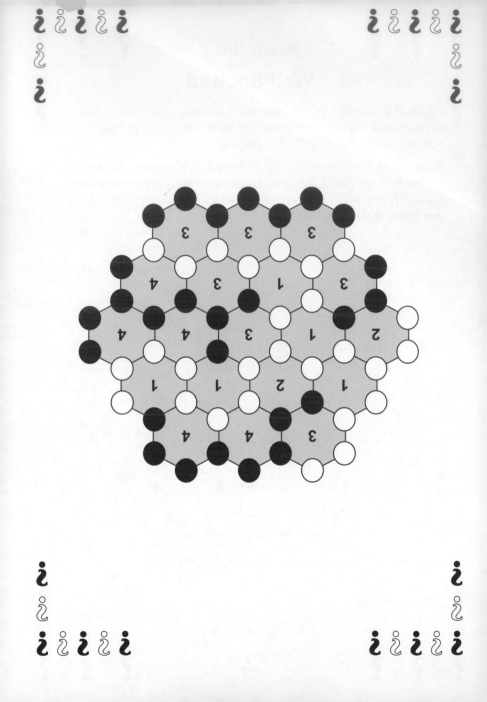

Alphafill

Place 25 different letters of the alphabet, one per circle, in order to spell out the listed words. Words are formed by moving between adjacent circles along the connecting lines, either horizontally, vertically or diagonally in any direction.

Begin by crossing out the letters already in place, together with the one letter that doesn't appear in any of the words.

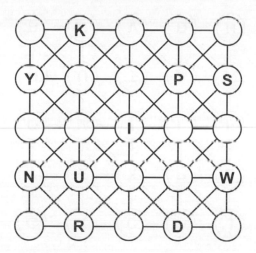

A B C D E F G H I J K L M
N O P Q R S T U V W X Y Z

BUT	FLIPS	JOCKEY	VAT
EQUIP	GEM	SLIME	WAD
EXIT	GYM	SPLIT	WAIT
FLAW	HAIL	TURN	WHAT

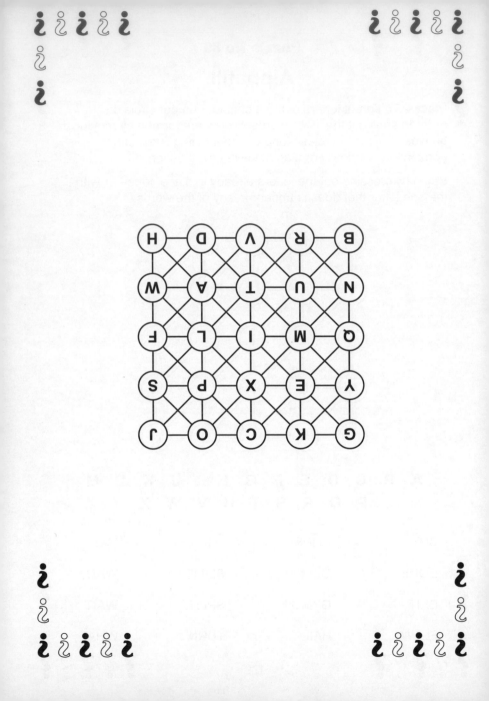

Hoshi

The numbers 1 to 9 must be placed into the individual cells of each of the six large triangles.

No digit can appear more than once in any horizontal row or diagonal line of any length, even those rows and lines that are interrupted by the central hexagon.

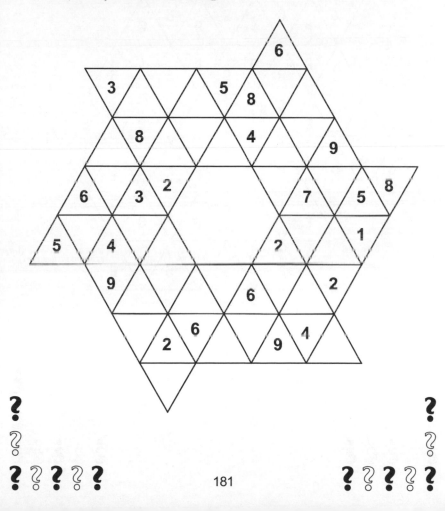

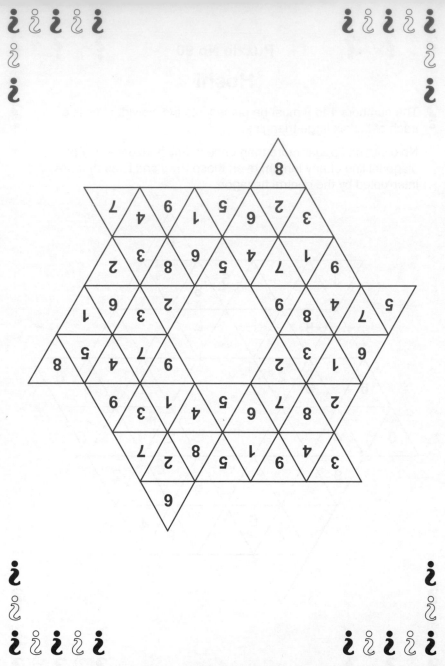

Pieceword

This crossword has been cut into 24 pieces. Can you reassemble it by placing the remaining 20 pieces?

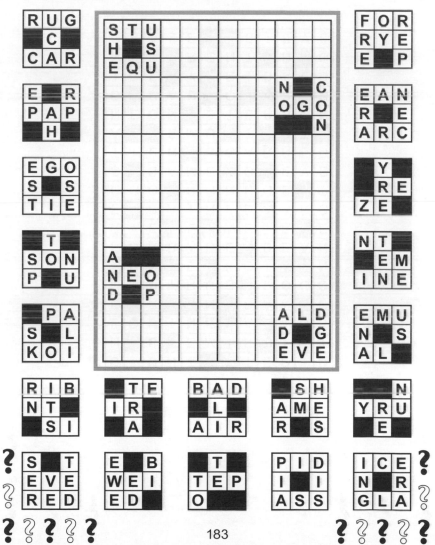

S	T	U	N	T			T	E	P	I	D
H		S		E	M	I	R		I		I
E	Q	U	I	N	E		A		A	S	S
E		R			N		P	A	N		C
P	A	P	Y	R	U	S		L	O	G	O
	H			E		K	O	I			N
F	O	R	B	A	D	E		B	E	A	N
R	Y	E		L		W	E	I	R		E
E		P	A	I	R	E	D		A	R	C
E	G	O		S	H	R	U	G	S		T
S		S	A	M	E		C		E	V	E
T	I	E	R		S	C	A	R	R	E	D
A			E	M	U		T			T	
N	E	O	N		S	T	E	P	S	O	N
D		P	A	L		O			P		U
I	C	E		Y		R	I	B	A	L	D
N		R		R	E	N	T		D		G
G	L	A	Z	E			S	I	E	V	E

S Bend

Place the letters of each word, one per cell, so that every word flows in a clockwise direction around a number. Where the hexagons of one word overlap with those of another, the letter in each cell is common to both.

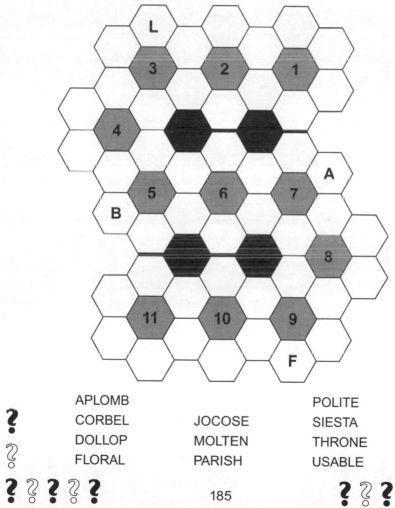

APLOMB		POLITE
CORBEL	JOCOSE	SIESTA
DOLLOP	MOLTEN	THRONE
FLORAL	PARISH	USABLE

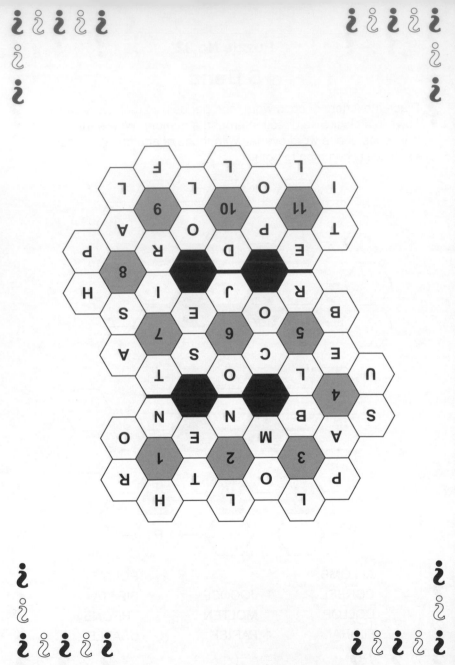

Loose Vowels

Every clue in this crossword consists of its solution, with the letters in order but minus its vowels. Your task is to replace the vowels; gd lck!

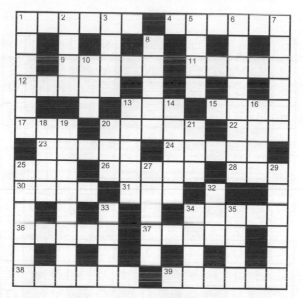

ACROSS

1 CHC (6)
4 MNT (6)
9 RD (5)
11 LD (5)
12 TR (5)
13 P (3)
15 RL (4)
17 DT (3)
20 FLS (5)
22 DY (3)
23 BRN (5)
24 SNR (5)
25 PT (3)
26 DGD (5)
28 DW (3)
30 LTS (4)
31 RT (3)
34 CBR (5)
36 BV (5)
37 BT (5)
38 NDR (6)
39 LNTL (6)

DOWN

1 CTD (6)
2 KR (4)
3 CD (4)
5 ML (4)
6 NLDD (8)
7 TDLY (6)
8 HTL (5)
10 RM (3)
13 PND (5)
14 SST (5)
16 RR (4)
18 B (4)
19 TTTD (8)
20 F (3)
21 ND (3)
25 PLS (6)
27 GRN (5)
29 WSL (6)
32 JT (3)
33 YR (4)
34 CG (4)
35 BT (4)

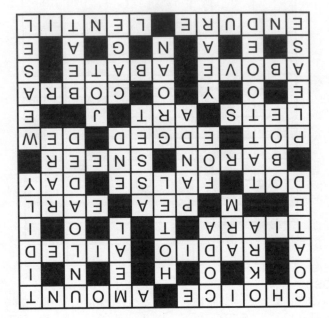

Skyscrapers

Place the numbers 1 to 7 into each row and column. Each number represents a skyscraper of that many floors. Organize the skyscrapers in such a way that the given number outside the grid represents the number of buildings which can be seen from that point, looking only at that number's row or column.

A skyscraper with a lower number of floors cannot hide a higher building, but one with a higher number of floors always hides any building behind it.

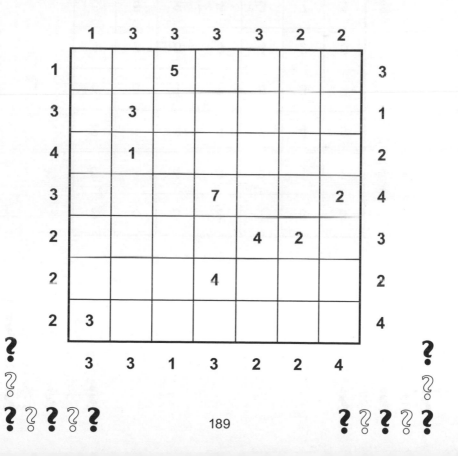

4	5	6	1	7	2	3
1	7	3	4	2	5	6
5	2	4	3	6	7	1
2	3	5	7	1	6	4
6	4	7	5	3	1	2
7	1	2	6	4	3	5
3	6	1	2	5	4	7

Number Cruncher

Just like a regular crossword, but with numbers as answers!

ACROSS

1 16 Across multiplied by three (4)

4 13 Across multiplied by three (4)

7 2 Down minus three eighths of 2 Down (2)

8 22 Down minus one third of 5 Down (2)

9 237 squared plus 8 Across plus 22 Down (5)

12 Yards in four furlongs (3)

13 12 Across plus one (3)

14 6 Down multiplied by four (5)

15 28 squared (3)

16 One thirteenth of 25 Across (3)

18 193 squared plus 22 Down plus double 7 Across (5)

21 One sixteenth of 15 Across (2)

23 Months in seven years (2)

24 94 squared plus 112 (4)

25 12 Across plus 15 Down minus 11 (4)

DOWN

1 Ounces in seven stone (4)

2 One eleventh of 12 Across (2)

3 15 Across plus two (3)

4 22 Down plus 5 Down plus 23 Across plus four (3)

5 Pints in six gallons (2)

6 1 Across plus 1 Down minus four (4)

9 224 squared minus one third of 22 Down (5)

10 21 Across multiplied by 3 Down (5)

11 136 squared minus one third of 23 Across (5)

15 13 Across multiplied by eight (4)

17 97 squared plus 38 (4)

19 3 Down plus one quarter of 5 Down (3)

20 16 Across minus double 23 Down (3)

22 8 Across plus one third of 5 Down (2)

23 23 Across minus three (2)

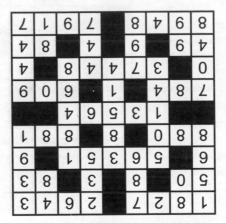

Round Numbers

Fill the circles so that every row and column of eight circles contains the numbers 1–8 inclusive. The shaded circles contain odd numbers 1, 3, 5 and 7, and the white circles contain even numbers 2, 4, 6 and 8. Some of the numbers are already in place.

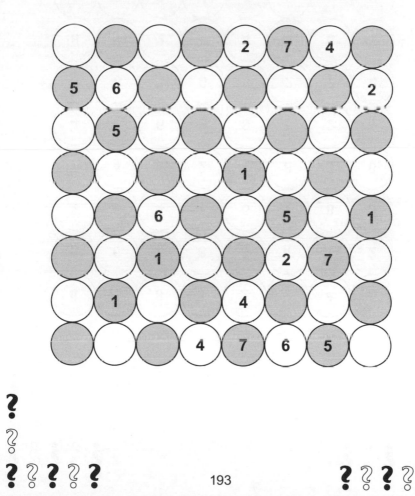

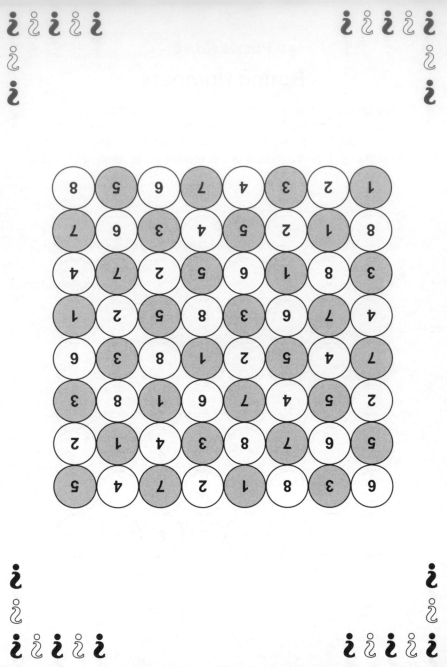

Combiku

Each horizontal row and vertical column should contain five different shapes and five different numbers. Every square will contain one number and one shape and no combination may be repeated anywhere else in the puzzle: for example, if a square has both a 4 and a star, then no other square will contain both a 4 and a star.

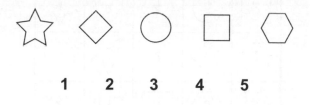

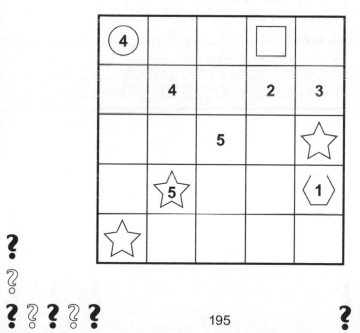

Latin Square

Fill the grid with numbers from 1 to 6, so that each number appears exactly once in every row and every column.

The clues refer to the sum of the numbers in the squares mentioned: for example, B C D 1 = 14 means that the numbers in squares B1, C1 and D1 add up to 14.

1 D 4 5 = 8

2 E F 1 = 6

3 B 1 2 3 = 11

4 D E 3 = 11

5 B C 4 = 5

6 E 4 5 = 9

7 A B 5 = 7

8 F 3 4 = 6

9 C 2 3 = 5

10 D E 2 = 4

11 A 2 3 4 = 6

12 C D 3 = 6

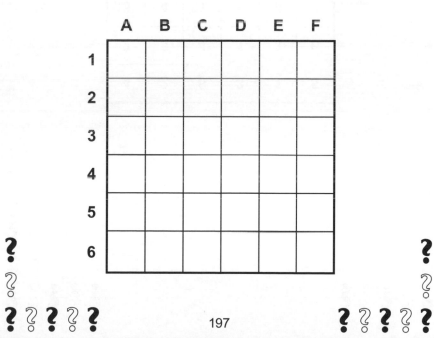

4	2	6	3	1	5
2	5	4	1	3	6
3	4	1	5	6	2
1	3	2	6	5	4
6	1	5	2	4	3
5	6	3	4	2	1

Battleships

Can you place the vessels into the diagram? Some parts of vessels or sea squares have already been filled in. A number to the left or above a row or column refers to the number of occupied squares in that row or column.

Any vessel may be positioned horizontally or vertically, but no part of a vessel touches part of any other vessel, either horizontally, vertically or diagonally.

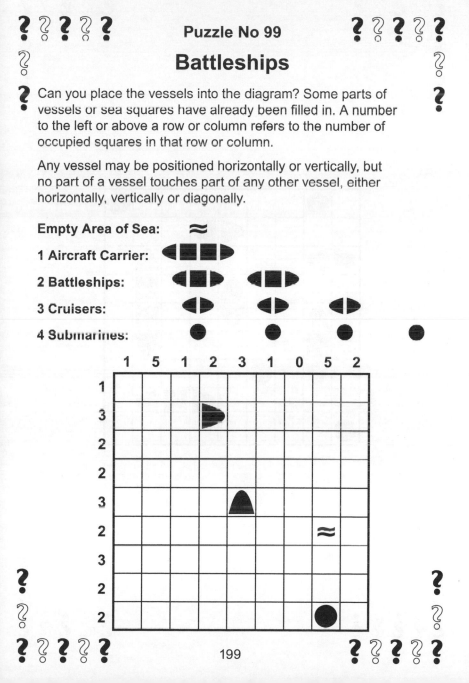

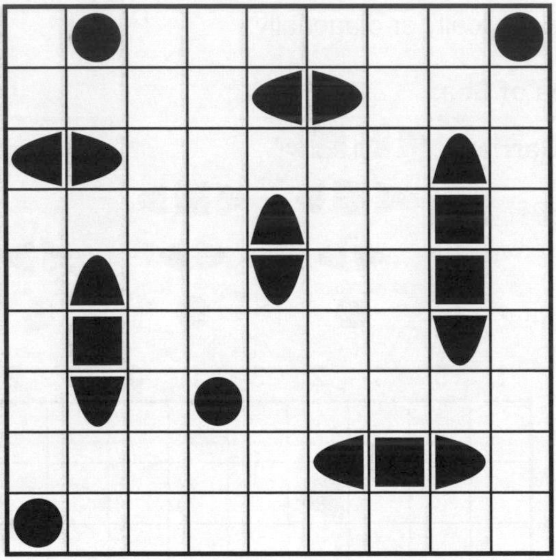

Arrowword

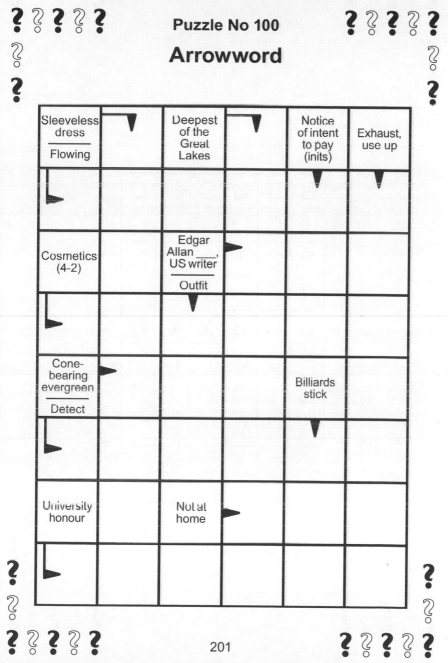

D	E	G	R	E	E
	R	O	U	T	
N	O	T	I	C	E
	F	I	R	E	L
M	A	K	E	U	P
N	P	O	E		
L	I	Q	U	I	D
P		S			

Shape Up

Every row and column in this grid originally contained one circle, one diamond, one square, one triangle and two blank squares, although not necessarily in that order.

Every symbol with a black arrow refers to the first of the four symbols encountered when travelling in the direction of the arrow. Every symbol with a white arrow refers to the second of the four symbols encountered in the direction of the arrow.

Can you complete the original grid?

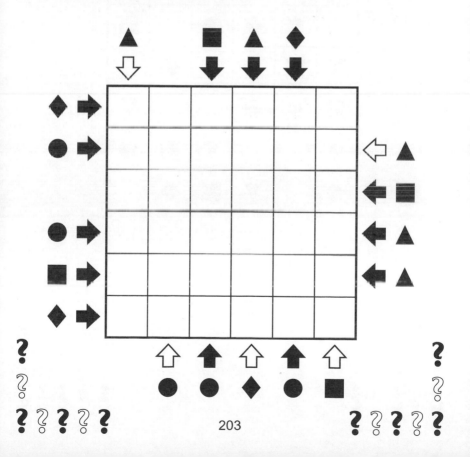

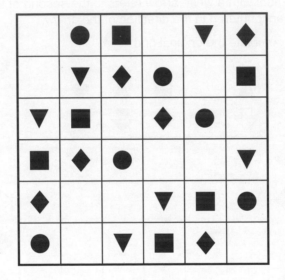

Domino Placement

A standard set of 28 dominoes has been laid out as shown. Can you draw in the edges of them all? The check-box is provided as an aid and the domino already placed may help.

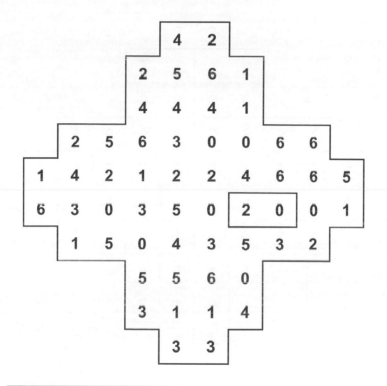

0-0	0-1	0-2	0-3	0-4	0-5	0-6	1-1	1-2	1-3	1-4	1-5	1-6	2-2
		✓											

2-3	2-4	2-5	2-6	3-3	3-4	3-5	3-6	4-4	4-5	4-6	5-5	5-6	6-6

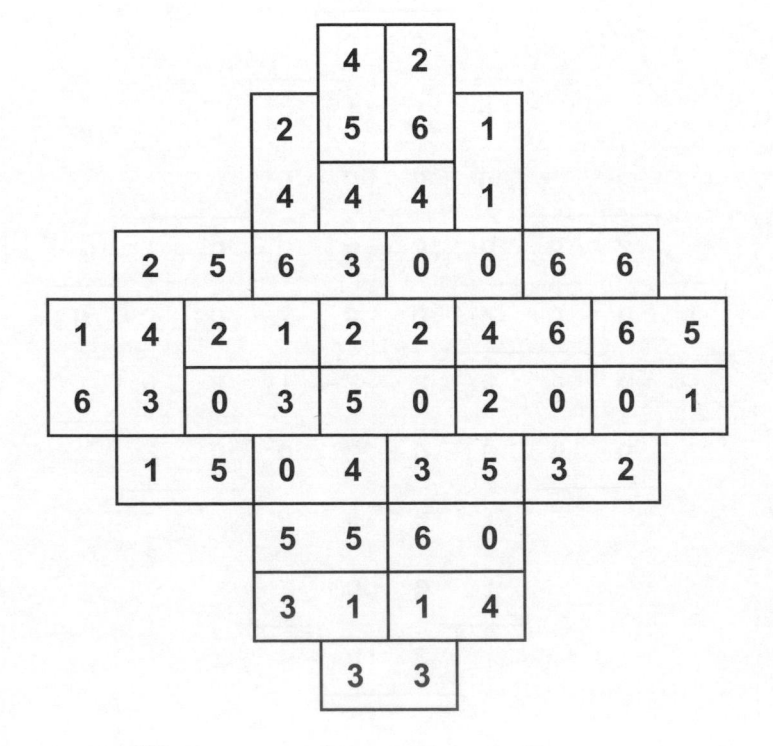

Codeword

Every letter in this crossword has been replaced by a number, the number remaining the same for that letter wherever it occurs in the grid. Can you substitute numbers for letters and complete the crossword? It may help to cross off the letters either side of the grid to keep track of progress, and the reference box showing which numbers have been decoded can also aid solving. Three letters have already been entered into the grid, to help you on your way.

	1	2	3	4	5	6	7	8	9	10	11	12	13	
A	3	18	15	11	25	■	7	11	21	13	19	3	4	**N**
B	25	■	3	■	5	■	11	■	15	■	22	■	5	**O**
C	9	5	26	20	3	12	16	■	3	12	13	7	5	**P**
D	11	■	11	■	7	■	20	■	16	■	5	■	9	**Q**
E	22	12	21	11	14	17	11	25	16	3	18	7	5	**R**
F	26	■	■	26	■	■	12	■	5	■	11	■	9	**S**
G	■	1	16	3	25	16	■	24	25	11 **O**	8	10	■	**T**
H	1	■	25	■	15	■	24	■	24 **P**	■	■	13		**U**
I	23	22	3	7	20	17	20	21	3	16 **I**	20	11	12	**V**
J	22	■	20	■	2	■	16	■	24	■	9	■	11	**W**
K	20	6	7	11	11	■	20	14	24	25	20	12	16	**X**
L	26	■	6	■	14	■	5	■	7	■	11	■	10	**Y**
M	16	3	25	6	5	16	1	■	5	12	16	25	10	**Z**

1	2	3	4	5	6	7	8	9	10	11 O	12	13
14	15	16 T	17	18	19	20	21	22	23	24 P	25	26

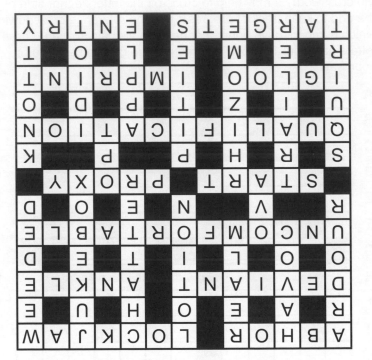

Calcudoku

Each row and column should contain the numbers 1–6. The numbers placed in a heavily outlined set of squares may be repeated, but must produce the calculation in the top left corner, using the mathematical symbol provided. So, for example, when multiplied, the numbers 3 and 4 total 12:

x12	
4	3

Any block of one square will contain the number in the top left corner.

x12		+8		+15	
	x3				ı11
+17		x6			
		−1		/2	
/5	x120		/3	x3	
				x24	

4	9	2	3	5	1
3	1	9	4	2	5
1	2	5	6	4	3
5	3	1	2	6	4
6	5	4	1	3	2
2	4	3	5	1	6

Puzzle No 105
Piecework

Place all of the pieces into the grid. Any may be rotated or flipped over, but none may touch another, not even diagonally at a corner.

The numbers outside the grid refer to the number of consecutive black squares; and each block is separated from the others by at least one white square. For instance, '3 2' could refer to a row with either none or any number of white squares, then three black squares, then at least one white square, then two more black squares, followed by either none or any number of white squares.

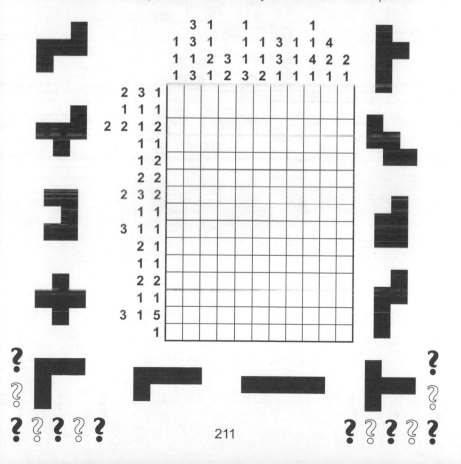

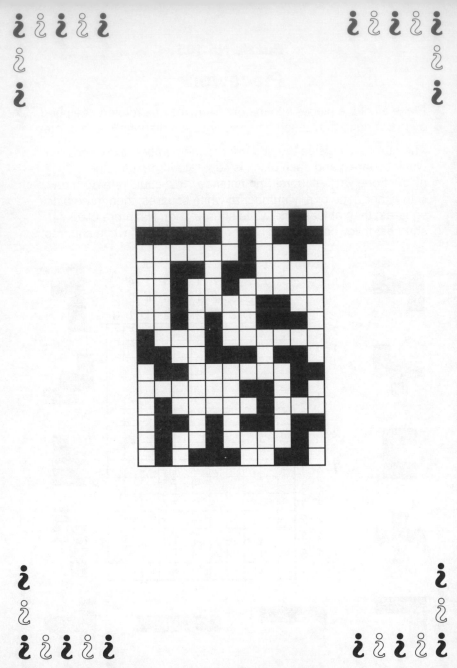

Tile Twister

Place the eight tiles into the puzzle grid so that all adjacent numbers on each tile match up. Tiles may be rotated through 360 degrees, but none may be flipped over.

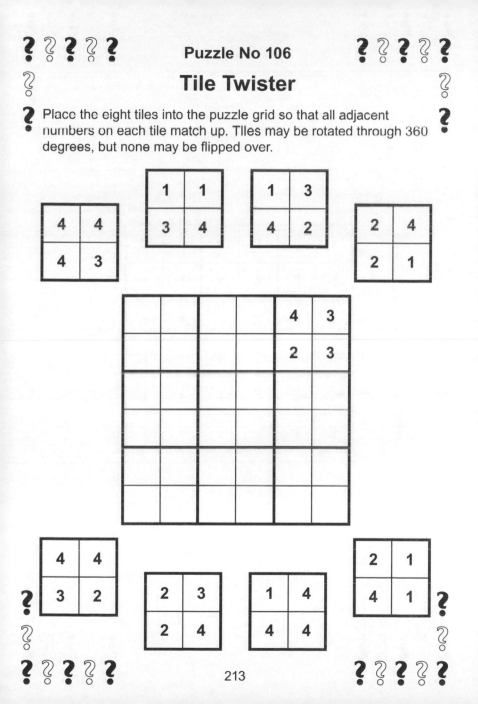

3	1	1	4	4	3
4	1	1	2	2	3
4	1	1	2	2	3
4	4	4	2	2	4
4	4	4	2	2	4
3	4	4	3	3	1

Box Clever

When the shape below is folded to form a cube, just one of the lettered alternatives can be produced. Which?

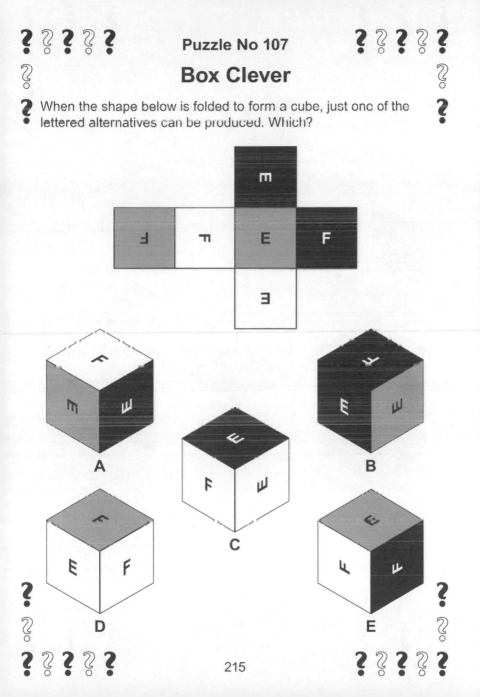

A

B

C

D

E

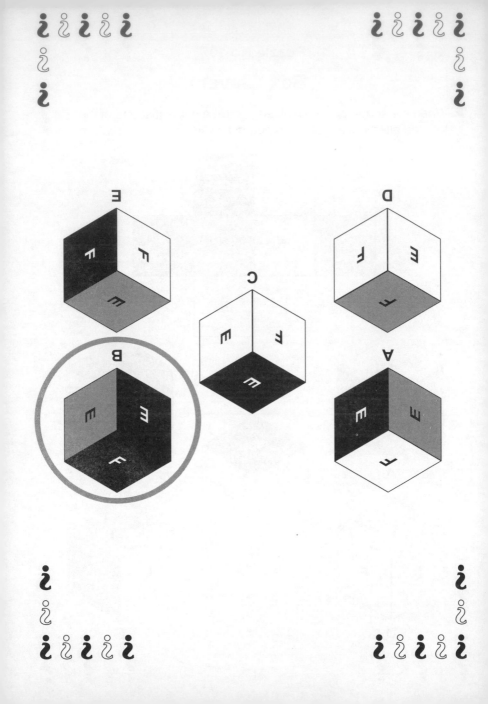

Four Out of Three

Fill the grid using the three-letter words. When they've been entered correctly, three four-letter words will be revealed in each row, reading from left to right.

E	A	R				E	N	D			
V	A	N				A	N	T			
T	O	O				L	E	K			
S	P	A				A	M	P			
P	R	O				R	A	G			
D	I	E				R	O	B			
K	I	N				Z	E	N			
C	U	R				T	H	Y			
M	E	N				A	R	M			
S	U	N				T	O	W			

URN	OUR	OAT	NOT	HIM
GUN	IRK	RUB	DAD	HUG
ICE	LUG	BOA	LAM	THE
EEL	USE	TAB	WOK	RIM

? ? ? ? ?
? ? ? ? ?

E	A	R	L	A	M	E	N	D	I	R	K
V	A	N	E	E	L	A	N	T	H	U	G
T	O	O	T	A	B	L	E	K	N	O	T
S	P	A	R	I	M	A	M	P	L	U	G
P	R	O	W	O	K	R	A	G	R	U	B
D	I	E	T	H	E	R	O	B	U	R	N
K	I	N	D	A	D	Z	E	N	I	C	E
C	U	R	B	O	A	T	H	Y	O	U	R
M	E	N	U	S	E	A	R	M	O	A	T
S	U	N	G	U	N	T	O	W	H	I	M

Light Up

Place circles (representing light bulbs) in some of the empty squares, in such a way that no two bulbs shine on each other, until every square of the grid is lit up. A bulb sends rays of light horizontally and vertically, illuminating its entire row and column unless its light is blocked by a black cell.

Some black cells contain numbers, indicating how many light bulbs are in adjacent squares either immediately above, below, to the right or to the left. Bulbs placed diagonally adjacent to a numbered cell do not contribute to the bulb count. An unnumbered black cell may have any number of light bulbs adjacent to it, or none at all, and not all light bulbs are necessarily clued via black squares.

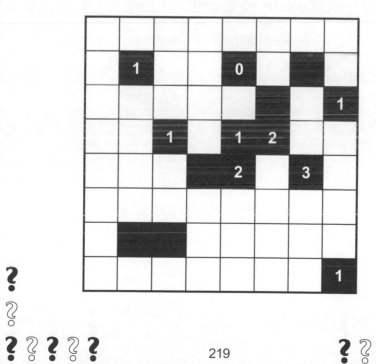

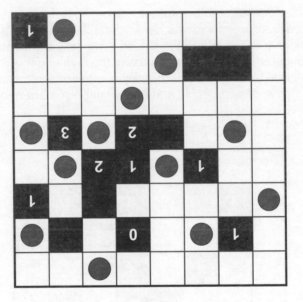

Kakuro

Using single digits from 1 to 9 inclusive, fill the grid so that the numbers in each block add up to the total in the box above or to the left of it. No digit may be used twice in a block. The same digit may occur more than once in a row or column, but it must be in a separate block.

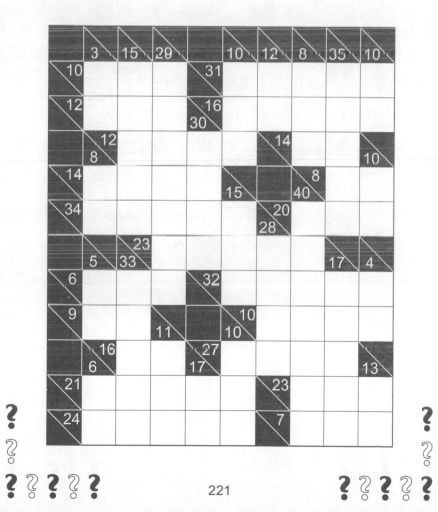

2	3	5			7	9	1	8	6
1	5	6			1	3	2	6	4
	1	3	6	2		5	9		
1	2	4	7					7	1
7	4	8	9	6			6	5	9
		2	8	1	7	5			
2	3	1			8	9	7	5	3
3	6					4	3	2	1
	9	7		7	8	9	3		
2	7	3	8	1			8	6	9
4	8	1	9	2			2	1	4

Slitherlink

Draw a single continuous loop, by connecting the dots. No line may cross the path of another.

The figure inside each set of any four surrounding dots indicates the total number of surrounding lines.

```
.    .    .    .    .    .    .    .    .    .    .    .
          3              2              3
.    .    .    .    .    .    .    .    .    .    .    .
   2    2    2    2    2              3         2    2
.    .    .    .    .    .    .    .    .    .    .    .
                  2    1                   1    2    2
.    .    .    .    .    .    .    .    .    .    .    .
   3              0    2    2         0              3
.    .    .    .    .    .    .    .    .    .    .    .
   3              1         0    2
.    .    .    .    .    .    .    .    .    .    .    .
                  1    2         2         3    2
.    .    .    .    .    .    .    .    .    .    .    .
        2    1    2         3
.    .    .    .    .    .    .    .    .    .    .    .
             0    3         2    2              2
.    .    .    .    .    .    .    .    .    .    .    .
   3                             2         2    2    2
.    .    .    .    .    .    .    .    .    .    .    .
             2    3    1    2    2    1    2
.    .    .    .    .    .    .    .    .    .    .    .
   1         2    2         2         1    1         3
.    .    .    .    .    .    .    .    .    .    .    .
             3                   2              2
.    .    .    .    .    .    .    .    .    .    .    .
        2    3              3
.    .    .    .    .    .    .    .    .    .    .    .
```

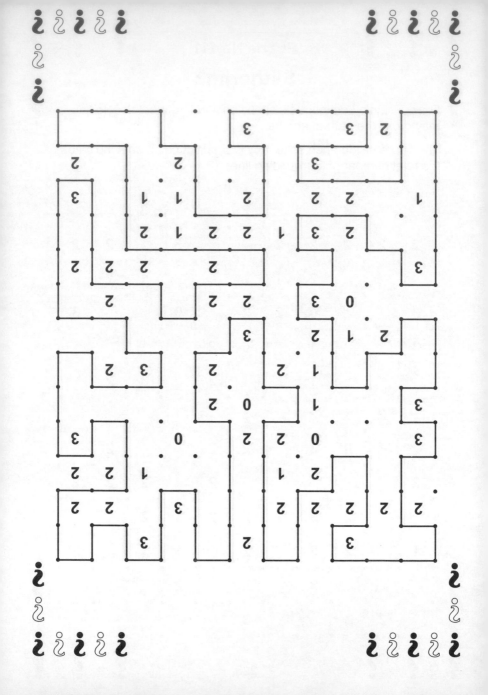

Egg Timer

Can you complete this puzzle in the time that it takes to boil an egg? The answers to the clues are anagrams of the words immediately above and below, plus or minus a letter.

1 Enclosed
2 Climb up
3 Chair carried on poles
4 Fine, loosely ground rock
5 Natives of Denmark
6 Make unhappy
7 Urgent requests

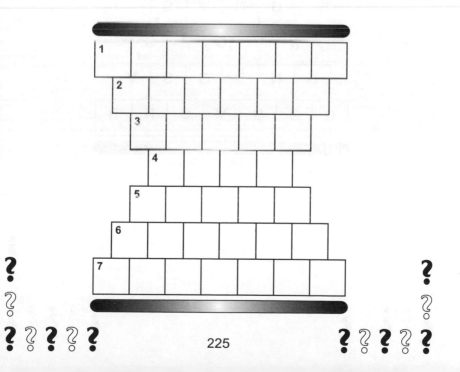

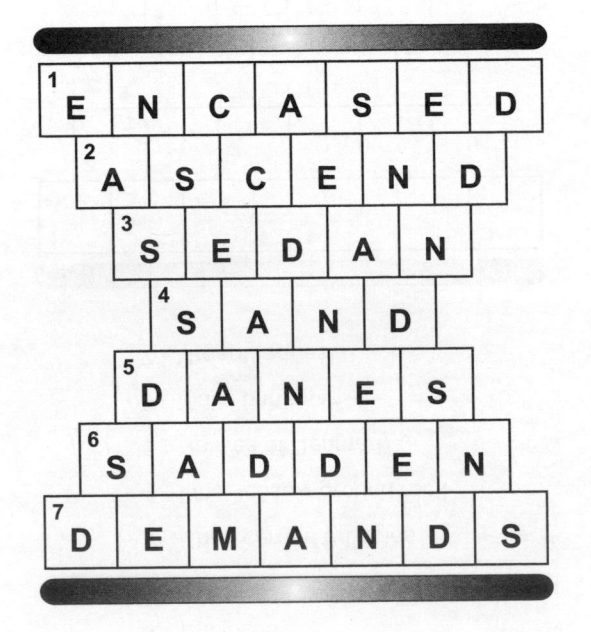

General Knowledge Crossword

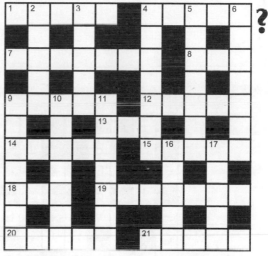

ACROSS

1 Birthplace of Muhammad (5)

4 Italian operatic composer (1813–1901) (5)

7 Country, capital Dakar (7)

8 Ms Gardner, Hollywood actress (1922–90) (3)

9 Having a sharp inclination (5)

12 Dickens character in *David Copperfield*, ___ Heep (5)

13 Scottish resort and fishing port (3)

14 Postal abbreviation for Shropshire (5)

15 Legionary emblem (5)

18 Clairvoyance (inits) (3)

19 Dug up for reburial or for medical investigation (7)

20 Ancient upright stone slab bearing markings (5)

21 Bird associated with the Tower of London (5)

DOWN

2 Eliminate from the body (5)

3 Mediterranean island associated with the Minoan civilization (5)

4 Bird with a naked head which feeds chiefly on carrion (7)

5 Town on the River Thames in Berkshire (7)

6 Sir Walter Scott novel of 1819 (7)

9 Members of a religious order of women (7)

10 Obstruction of one heavenly body by another (7)

11 Capital of French Polynesia, on the north-west coast of Tahiti (7)

16 Caribbean island, capital Oranjestad (5)

17 Province of eastern Belgium (5)

Around the Block

You won't need a starting block to get you under way, because it isn't a race! Just arrange the six-letter solutions to the clues into the six blocks around each clue number.

Write the answers in a clockwise or anticlockwise direction and you'll find that the last answer fits into the first; the problem is to decide in which square to put the first letter of each word...

1 Stick to

2 Cancel, rescind

3 Gradually acquire new traits or characteristics

4 Pass from physical life

5 Transfer abroad, as with goods

6 Firm, constant, unwavering

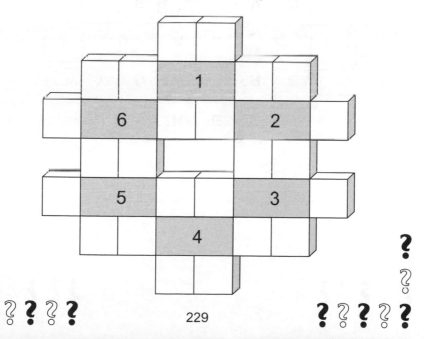

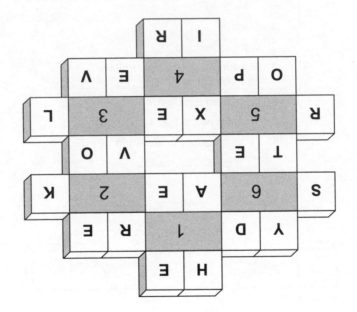

1 Adhere (c), 2 Revoke (a/c), 3 Evolve (c),
4 Expire (a/c), 5 Export (c), 6 Steady (a/c)

Puzzle No 115

Eliminator

Every oval shape contains a different letter of the alphabet from A to K inclusive. Use the clues to determine their locations. Reference in the clues to 'due' means in any location along the same horizontal or vertical line.

1 H is due east of E, which is due north of F, which is due east of G.

2 J is due north of C, which is next to and west of I, which is due north of A.

3 K is next to and north of D, which is next to and east of F.

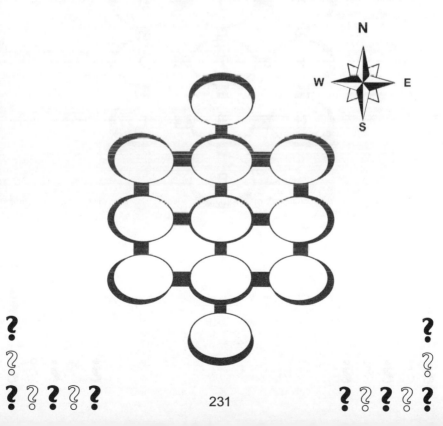

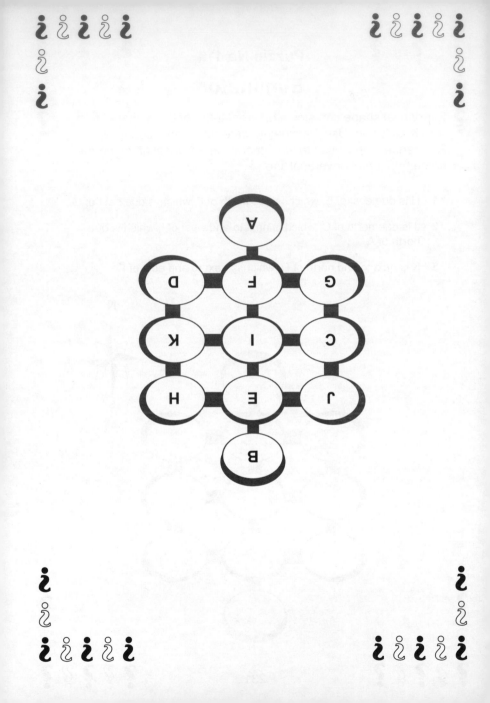

Figure It Out

Every square in the grid is to be filled with a single digit number from 1 to 9 – each of those numbers being used four times. Use the clues to complete the grid, bearing in mind that the same number must not appear in two adjacent (touching) squares either across or down. If the same number is used more than once in any row across or column down, it is stated in the relevant clue.

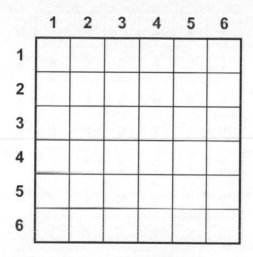

ACROSS

1 Total twenty-one.
2 Two *ones*. Two *twos*. No *four*.
3 Consecutive numbers placed in order.
4 Two *fives*. No *one*.
5 Two *threes*. Two *nines*. No *eight*.
6 Two *sevens*. No *two*.

DOWN

1 *Two* is the only even number.
2 Two *twos*. No *five*.
3 Total thirty-nine.
4 Total thirty-three.
5 Two *sixes* are the only even numbers.
6 Two *eights*. No *three*. No *five*.

8	9	7	4	9	7	9
1	3	4	9	3	9	5
9	6	5	8	2	5	4
8	7	6	5	4	3	3
2	1	8	7	2	1	2
4	5	3	6	1	2	1
6	5	4	3	2	1	

Round Up

The number in each circle is the sum of the two numbers below it. Just work out the missing numbers in every circle!

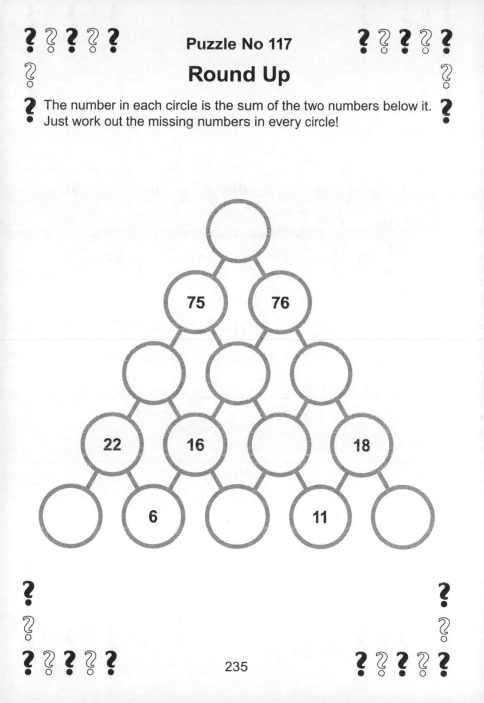

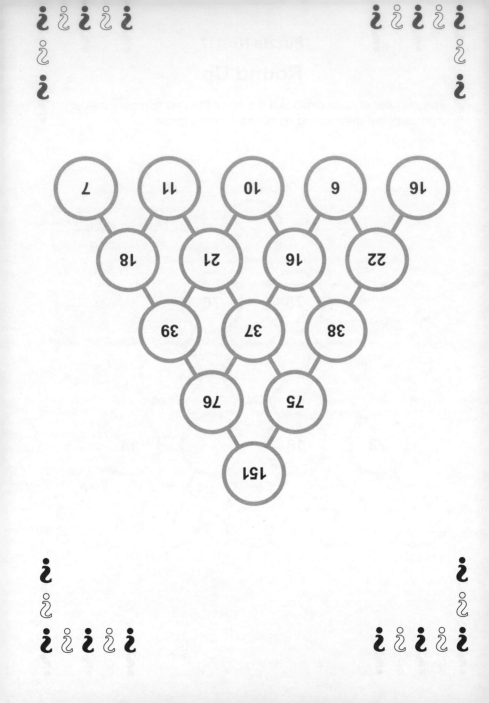

Windows

There is a four-letter word hidden in each of the boxes on the left that can only be revealed by matching each box with its correct window-strip on the right. Can you match all ten?

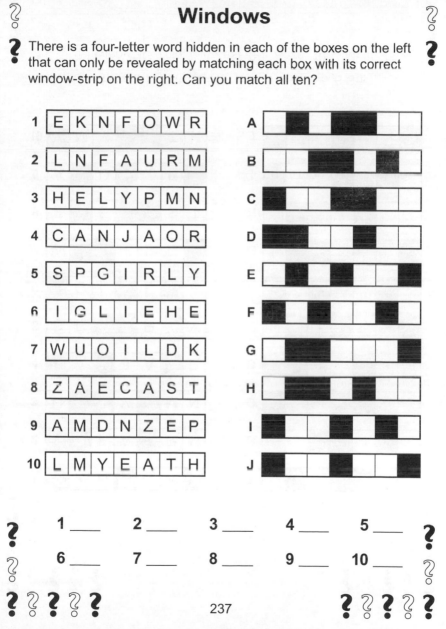

| 1 | E | K | N | F | O | W | R |

A

| 2 | L | N | F | A | U | R | M |

B

| 3 | H | E | L | Y | P | M | N |

C

| 4 | C | A | N | J | A | O | R |

D

| 5 | S | P | G | I | R | L | Y |

E

| 6 | I | G | L | I | E | H | E |

F

| 7 | W | U | O | I | L | D | K |

G

| 8 | Z | A | E | C | A | S | T |

H

| 9 | A | M | D | N | Z | E | P |

I

| 10 | L | M | Y | E | A | T | H |

J

1 ___   2 ___   3 ___   4 ___   5 ___

6 ___   7 ___   8 ___   9 ___   10 ___

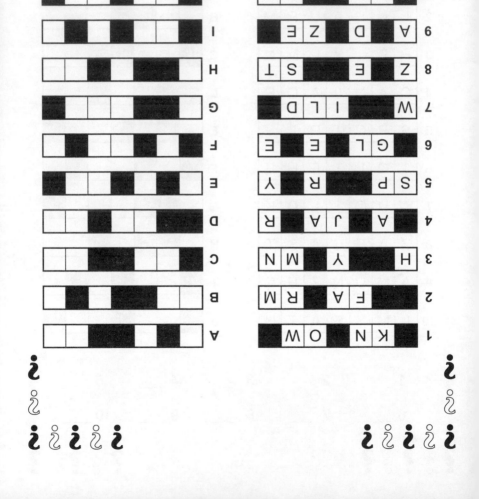

1-J Know, 2-D Farm, 3-H Hymn, 4-F Ajar, 5-B Spry,
6-I Glee, 7-G Wild, 8-A Zest, 9-E Adze, 10-C Myth

In Sequence

Which of the four alternatives (A, B, C or D) should take the place of the empty box in the sequence below?

5	14	15
17	6	7
12	3	2

1

7	3	6
2	12	14
5	17	15

2

14	17	12
15	5	3
7	2	6

3

?

4

3	2	15
6	7	17
14	5	12

A

3	2	5
6	17	7
14	15	12

B

3	2	5
6	7	17
14	15	12

C

3	12	5
6	7	17
14	15	2

D

5	14	15
17	6	7
12	3	2

1

7	3	6
2	12	14
5	17	15

2

14	17	12
15	5	3
7	2	6

3

3	2	5
6	7	17
14	15	12

C

The numbers move two places each time, working down the left column, up the central column and down the right column, with the final two numbers joining the top of the left column in the following sequence.

Chaindoku

Fill each empty circle with a number from 1 to 6 inclusive.

Each row, each column and each set of linked circles should contain six different numbers.

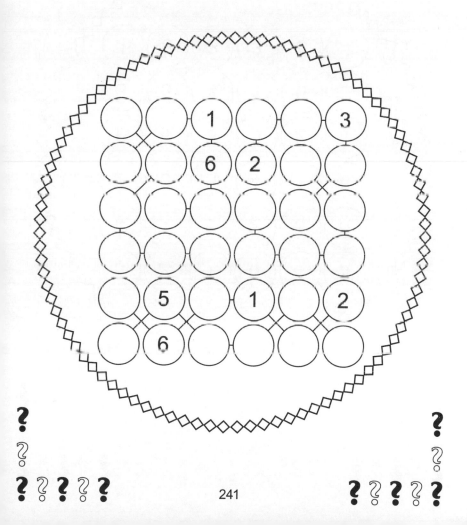

5	2	1	6	4	3
4	1	6	2	3	5
2	3	5	4	1	6
6	4	3	5	2	1
3	5	4	1	6	2
1	6	2	3	5	4

Logi-Nine

The numbers 1 to 9 inclusive should appear once in each row, as well as once in each column.

Every heavily outlined shape of nine smaller squares should also contain each of the numbers from 1 to 9.

Can you complete the grid?

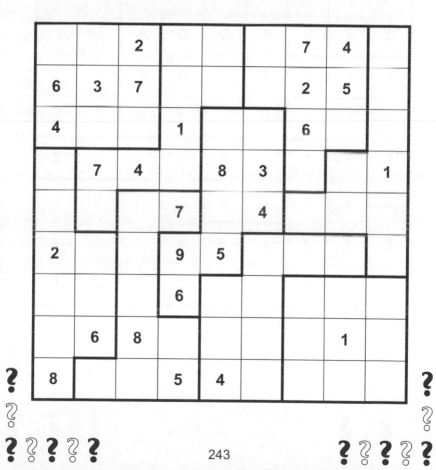

1	9	2	3	6	8	7	4	5
6	3	7	8	9	1	2	5	4
4	8	5	1	7	2	6	3	9
5	7	4	2	8	3	9	6	1
9	5	6	7	1	4	8	2	3
2	4	3	9	5	6	1	8	7
3	1	9	6	2	5	4	7	8
7	6	8	4	3	9	5	1	2
8	2	1	5	4	7	3	9	6

Word Ladders

In each of the word ladders below, change one letter at a time (but don't change the position of any letter) to make a new word – and move from the word at the top of the ladder to the word at the bottom using the exact number of rungs provided.

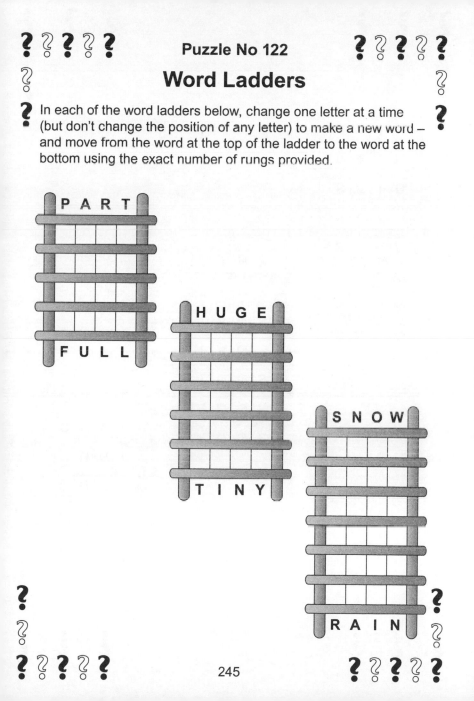

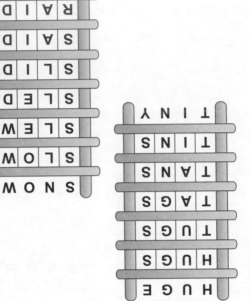

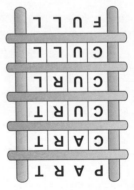

Puzzle No. 177

Word Ladders

Other solutions may be possible.

Hexafit

Can you place the hexagons into the grid, so that where any hexagon touches another along a straight line, the contents of both triangles are the same? No rotation of any hexagon is allowed!

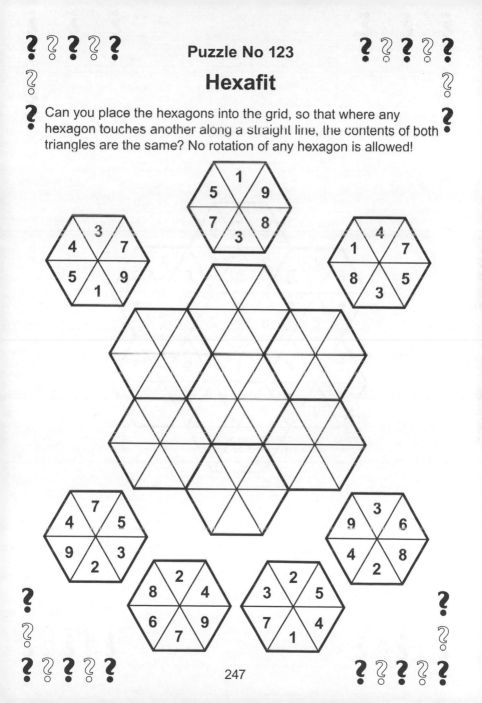

247

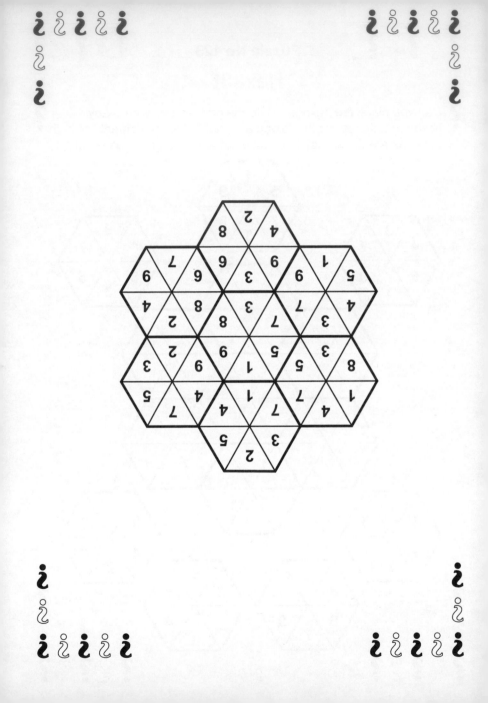

Coin Collecting

In this puzzle, an amateur coin collector has been out with his metal detector, searching for booty. He didn't have time to dig up all the coins he found, so has made a grid map, showing their locations, in the hope that if he loses the map, at least no one else will understand it... However, he didn't count on YOU coming across the strange grid (as seen here). Will you be able to discover the correct number of coins and their precise locations?

Those squares containing numbers are empty, but where a number appears in a square, it indicates how many coins are located in the squares (up to a maximum of eight) surrounding the numbered one, touching it at any corner or side. There is only one coin in any individual square. Place a circle into every square containing a coin.

			2						
3	5	6	6		3		1	0	1	
					2	2	2			0
	4	5				2	2		
1	2		2						0
	2	1		2		2		3	1
	1		3			1		2		2
2			3		2			2	
	3								2
3			3			3	5		5	
	3		1		2			5	
	1	1	1		4			3	1

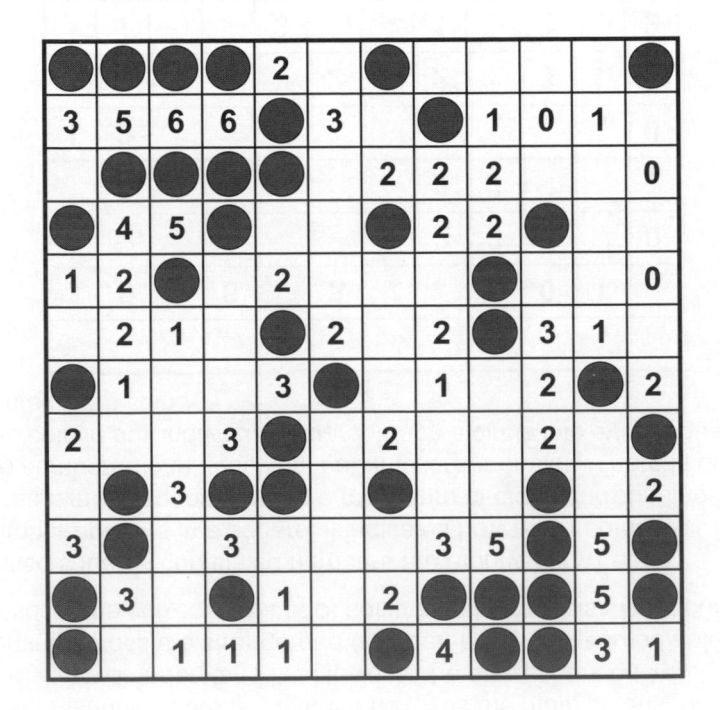

Holesome Fun

In this puzzle, you must find an eight-letter word by deciding which common letter has been removed from the trios of words. Place that letter into the hole at the end of each row and the word will be revealed reading downwards.

_ L U G	A _ S E	C A _ E	◯
P _ O T	J U _ Y	F _ A X	◯
_ P O N	G O _ T	_ S E R	◯
_ U C H	F O R _	_ I N T	◯
R U _ Y	O _ O E	A _ L E	◯
R _ S E	_ D L E	S A _ D	◯
O _ Y X	G _ A T	B A _ D	◯
E D _ E	O _ L E	_ L A D	◯

(G)	GLAD	OGLE	EDGE
(N)	BAND	GNAT	ONYX
(I)	SAID	IDLE	RISE
(B)	ABLE	OBOE	RUBY
(M)	MINT	FORM	MUCH
(U)	USER	GOUT	UPON
(L)	FLAX	JULY	PLOT
(P)	CAPE	APSE	PLUG

Simple as ABC?

Each of the small squares in the grid below contains either A, B or C. Every row, column and each of the two long diagonals has exactly two of each letter. To help you solve this problem, we have provided as many clues as we think you will need! Can you tell the letter in each square?

ACROSS

1 Any three consecutive squares contain three different letters.
2 The Cs are between the Bs.
3 Each B is directly next to and right of an A.
4 The Cs are further right than the As.
5 No clue.
6 No clue.

DOWN

1 The Cs are between the As.
2 Any three consecutive squares contain three different letters.
3 The As are higher than the Bs.
4 The Bs are higher than the Cs.
5 The As are higher than the Bs.
6 The Bs are between the Cs.

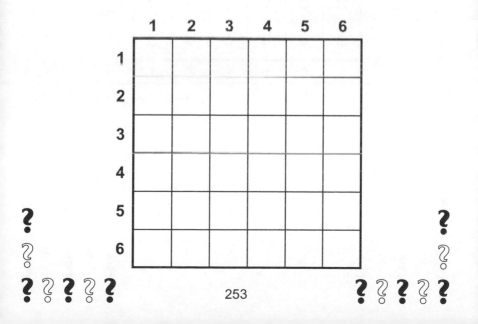

	1	2	3	4	5	6
1	B	A	C	B	A	C
2	A	B	C	A	C	B
3	C	C	A	B	A	B
4	B	A	A	C	B	C
5	C	B	B	A	C	A
6	A	C	B	C	B	A

Zigzag

The object of this puzzle is to trace a single path from the top left corner to the bottom right corner of the grid, travelling through all of the cells (tracking through the numbers in the sequence 1-2-3-4-5-6-7-8-1-2-3-4-5-6-7-8, etc) in either a horizontal, vertical or diagonal direction.

1	2	3	6	4	3	1	8
5	4	3	5	7	2	5	7
6	4	2	8	1	4	3	6
7	1	5	1	2	3	1	2
8	6	6	8	2	6	4	8
1	7	7	5	3	5	7	5
2	8	5	6	4	4	6	7
3	4	7	8	1	2	3	8

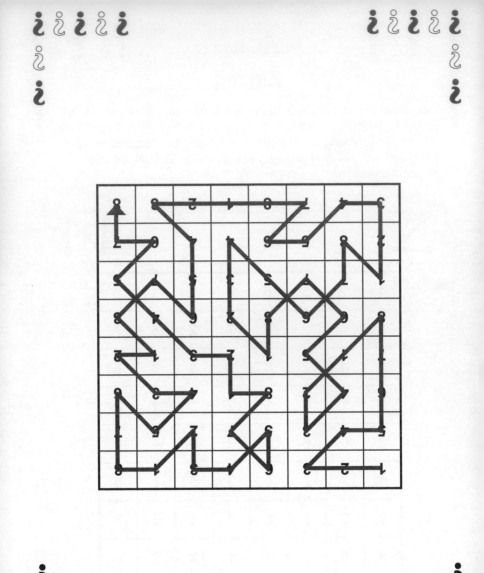